SOME MOTHERS DO HAVE
OTHERS DON'T

Some Mothers Do Have 'Em . . . Others Don't

A Christian approach to childlessness and infertility

Hugo & Sharon Anson

eagle
Guildford, Surrey

British Library Cataloguing in Publication Data. A catalogue
record for this book is available from the British Library.

Published by Eagle, an imprint of Inter Publishing Service
(IPS) Ltd, St Nicholas House, 14 The Mount, Guildford, Surrey
GU2 5HN.

Typeset by Palimpsest Book Production Limited,
Polmont, Stirlingshire

Printed by Caledonian International Book Manufacturing

ISBN No: 0 86347 212 5

ACKNOWLEDGMENTS

Many people have helped us put this book together. Some by prayer and encouragement, others let us interview them, still others let us put their story in the text. We believe that the book will be used by the Lord Jesus to help many Christians and others to either overcome their circumstances, or overcome in their circumstances. So, in both His name and ours, thank you all.

Particular thanks go to our medical consultant **Dr Catherine Sweatman**. We are not doctors and therefore her input into chapters 5 and 10 was essential. In the same breath we must acknowledge our debt to **Professor Lord Winston** (the well known fertility expert often seen on television) for letting us draw from his excellent book *Getting Pregnant* (Pan). It is both readable and informative and we recommend it to anyone as a text book that is accessible to the non medical mind. At times he explains his understanding of the ethical rights and wrongs that relate to infertility treatment; as Christians this does not always agree with our understanding, but is always informative and helpful.

That leaves our final and greatest debt of gratitude: **Jacqui Butler** and **Jonathan Booth**, who have led us through the minefield of how to get a book from brain to publishable state. They have worked and prayed hard and have always been encouraging.

Dedicated
to
Emma Louise

CONTENTS

Preface   viii
Introduction Our Story   1
Chapter 1   Does God Care That I Don't Have
              Children?   6
Chapter 2   Why Not Me?   11
Chapter 3   What Have I Done Wrong?   20
Chapter 4   As Jesus Said   26
Chapter 5   The Medical Maze   35
Chapter 6   Praying For Healing   54
Chapter 7   Gender Matters   71
Chapter 8   Mind Matters   88
Chapter 9   Hope Dead?   104
Chapter 10   Miscarriage and Still Birth   113
Chapter 11   Adoption?   123
Chapter 12   Every Cloud Has . . . ?   135
Chapter 13   But . . . But . . . But . . .   142
Chapter 14   One Day!   147

Further Reading   150
Notes   151

PREFACE

If we had been able to read this book sixteen years ago, it would have saved us from a great deal of confusion and pain as we wrestled with the issue of childlessness in our marriage for five years. Only those who have experienced the profound disappointment and grief that comes from the failure to have a baby can know what it is like. Sharon and Hugo, making themselves vulnerable through their honest sharing, have written a well-researched and practical book that will be enormously helpful both to couples facing childlessness and others who want to understand the experience.

This book offers great hope: that God's strength is made perfect in human weakness as we offer our lives to Him. The Ansons draw both from their own story and the experiences of others and we particularly commend them for their practical pro-life position in discussing the ethical issues surrounding fertility treatments.

We hope *Some Mothers Do Have 'Em . . . Others Don't* is widely read. It is a timely contribution to an increasingly complex moral and social issue. We recommend it. Practical, powerful, prophetic and not too technical it will help Christians towards an authentic biblical and practical understanding about childlessness.

Lyndon and Celia Bowring
January 1997

INTRODUCTION

OUR STORY

*Everyone should be quick to listen, slow
to speak and slow to become angry.*
(James 1:19)

T he service ended. The people started wandering towards
the coffee lounge. I felt a brief touch on my shoulder.

'Do you mind if I have a chat?' The woman standing over
me smiled. I relaxed. She introduced herself and sat down.
I had just been speaking in the Sunday morning meeting at
the end of a week of events in a friendly church.

'What's on your mind?' I asked.

'Sharon,' she started forcefully, 'I have some strong words
for you from the Lord.'

'Really:' The guards I keep around my tender heart went
back up!

'Sharon, I have thought about this long and hard and I
just know I have to say something. Well, it's like this . . .'
she stumbled, obviously nervous and excited all at the same
time. 'I was praying about you and your relationship with
Hugo, and the Lord showed me that you are proud!'

How kind of him, I thought wondering what was still
to come.

'You have pride in your heart. It is pride in your ability to
be free to minister, preach and travel. You are holding onto
this against God's will. You need to let it go! You need to
give your husband Hugo what he really wants in life, and
stop denying him!'

There was a pause for breath. Then a long stare. She was
trying to read my face.

'So what am I denying Hugo?' I asked wearily, knowing what was probably coming.

'Children! He wants family! And your pride and desire for a ministry career is stopping him!' She smiled with triumph. She had said what she came to say. Got it out of her system. Given God's Word!?

A brief wisp of doubt crossed her face.

What could I say to the poor lady? She was obviously very upset about something. This was her way to cope with it. I had to be nice and kind. But inside I wanted to thump her!

I had two objections.

Firstly *I am medically infertile.*

How dare she assume! She had not asked any questions or made any enquiries. Infertility is a very sensitive issue. Many fragile emotions are involved. Here she was accusing me of being a bad wife, on the basis that I did not have children. She could have been responsible for a nervous breakdown, suicide, the destruction of a good marriage or even, something far worse, a loss of faith in a loving God! You need to know that I object to Christians playing with other people's emotions like that! I hope you do too!

Secondly *The Lord Jesus' name had been taken in vain.*

She was taking God's name to give herself a cover for grinding her own axe. She wanted to have a go at me and she was using a pretence at prophecy to remove herself from having to take responsibility for her words.

This is very serious. People can live with or without children, but people cannot *live* without God. If we had not known God better, the way she behaved could have put us off knowing him at all. The fact is that God loves us and, even in a world with many things that are less than perfect, has a plan for our lives.

CAUSE?

I can't remember anybody actually telling me that I would probably not be able to have children. It was more like a process of absorbing the information slowly over the years.

At the age of 13 childbearing was not my highest priority. It was more a matter of beginning to understand my body, the feelings of puberty and knowing whether what I felt was normal or not.

For sometime I had pains which seemed to take hold of my stomach like a clamp. After a few investigations I was taken into a London hospital where the doctors opened me up and discovered cysts on both my ovaries.

I remember lying on my bed listening to Art Garfunkel singing 'I only have eyes for you' on *Top of the Pops*. My parents came in and informed me they had just been told they probably would not have grandchildren from this daughter. They say now that the doctor also came in and said this to me, but I don't remember that specifically; only that from that time on I knew that having children could well be a problem for me.

Being a Christian gave me a clear way of dealing with this. I simply dedicated my life to serve Jesus whatever the circumstances, putting my trust in him to sort this out if and when he wanted to.

MARRIAGE

I met Hugo when I was 21. I was already a full-time Christian speaker. I had been to college and then joined an organisation called Open Air Campaigners as a staff evangelist. The Lord had called me, opportunities were opening up and I was feeling fulfilled. Marriage was no longer the essential that this society portrays it to be. But it was still a very pleasant idea, as icing on the cake.

I remember asking Hugo a couple of weeks after we first met, 'How many children do you want?'

He said, 'Four?'!

I was worried. So we talked more. He eventually explained that the number four was thought up on the spur of the moment. He had been watching me all day and had noticed that I had spent most of the day playing with children. I like children and this had come across to him. He therefore said what he thought I wanted to hear!

I am sure Hugo and I have talked about children and childlessness more than most. Ninety per cent of that has been after we decided to write this book. Neither of us are saying that we wouldn't be intrigued to see what a child that was half Hugo and half me would look like. Neither of us are saying that there haven't been times when we've cried. Every now and then we have even started discussing the names we would give a child if one 'turned up'. We certainly wouldn't say that being infertile hasn't given us pressures and feelings of regret. But the honest truth is we are both very happy being the people we are, and doing the things we are doing.

THIS BOOK

That is the challenge of this book. Not so much how to get God to cure infertility; although we will examine how and when he sometimes does this. Not even how to be blissfully happy whether with children or not; although some people are. Rather, how to get a real understanding of who you are and how loving the true God is. To understand why the world is like it is regarding having children; and so to make sense of your place in God's plan. None of us can do everything or have every opportunity or joy in this fallen world. The important thing is to come to terms with this and be happy being the man or woman you are.

You will have questions.

Hopefully we will answer some of them. Some we will answer from the Bible – as this is the only place we can get any certainty about who God is, what he is like, and how his purposes work out in this world.

Other answers will come from the medical profession. After all they are the ones who know best how the biological functions of human reproductive organs work. They can also give us the information needed to help make informed ethical and moral decisions.

Still other questions, we will not so much answer as throw light upon; through telling more of our own story and the stories of many of our friends and saying how we or they have dealt with particular situations.

We are all different. But God is the same God for all of us.

People can be childless for all sorts of different medical, social, emotional or spiritual reasons. We shall examine a whole range of these, along with their accompanying difficulties and or solutions.

Our hope is quite simply that we shall help!

You may be childless yourself. It could be because you are single. It could be because of medical or sexual difficulties. It could be because you are obeying God's call on your life. Whatever the reason, whether voluntary or involuntary, chosen or forced upon you by circumstances; we hope this book will help *you*!

You may be a relative or friend of someone who is childless. You may even be a Christian or community leader and be concerned for those in your care who are beginning to realise they will have to face infertility in their lives. You want to have thought through the spiritual, medical and ethical issues. You want to know how God feels and somehow demonstrate this in the way you act on a day by day basis. You may even want to be able to lead your church in a way that somehow eliminates the kind of behaviour described at the beginning of this chapter. We think this book will help you.

So let's start asking the questions that need to be asked.

If we are honest the questions start with God. In a world where at least one in seven couples are experiencing infertility, where so many hearts are breaking the moment a period starts, where even Christian infertile couples don't always have their prayers answered, we ask: Does God care? Does God like children? Does infertility matter to God?

ONE

DOES GOD CARE THAT I DON'T HAVE CHILDREN?

'There are three things that are never satisfied, . . .
*. . . the grave, **the barren womb**,*
land, which is never satisfied with water,
and fire, which never says, 'Enough!'
(Prov 30: 15–16 our emphasis)

Y ES!
Yes God does care. He cares for your sake, because he loves you. He also cares because that is not the way it was meant to be. When he creates it is always with a purpose. He made reproductive organs with the ability to reproduce. His plan was that they should be used for reproduction. Of course he cares when their purpose and his plan fail to find fulfilment.

All of creation speaks the same story. 'In the beginning God created the heavens and the earth. Now the earth was formless and *empty [barren]*, darkness was over the surface of the deep, and the Spirit of God was hovering over the waters' (Gen 1:1, 2, our italics).

Creation starts empty. This is not a statement of purpose. It is a statement of intention. Anything empty is meant to be filled. You buy glasses empty – they are meant to be filled with drink. You buy clothes empty – they are meant to be filled with people.

So the problem is not emptiness. Rather it is when the emptiness remains longer than it is meant to.

It is not wrong for a person to remain childless for 10,

15, 20, 25 years, or even longer. The trouble comes when, in maturity, a person fails to conceive, having done all that is normally necessary.

In Genesis 1, for each container that God makes initially empty, he also provides something or someone to fill it! He takes the 'dry ground' (v 9–10) and fills it with 'seed-bearing plants and trees on the land that bear fruit with seed in it, according to their various kinds' (vv11–12). Having made the sky and the sea he then makes the birds and fish and commands them, 'Be fruitful and increase in number and fill the water in the seas, and let the birds increase on the earth' (v22).

Finally, having made mankind in his image (v27), the Lord goes on to command them (v28): 'Be fruitful and increase in number; fill the earth and subdue it.'

In other words, go and have children, then spread yourselves out until you fill every corner of the earth.

The instinct we all feel, to a lesser or greater degree, towards bearing children is not just physical, emotional or social, but deeply rooted in our nature and the purpose of our Creator.

When a couple is not able to have children something less than God's original plan is happening. His good and loving blueprint for their lives has been blocked. So, without it necessarily being their fault, something evil is happening to them.

SO WHAT WENT WRONG?

There are many evil things in this world. Anything less than the 'very good' original plan of God has to be described that way. Infertility is one sign of the corruption that has set in. Genesis 3 tells us how the rot started.

The root idea is sin. Not the sin of the individuals who are infertile. Mankind's original sin – rejection of simple obedience and friendship with God. God did not want this to happen. But free-will is an essential ingredient of love. God had done everything possible to persuade Adam and Eve not to use their ability to choose the wrong way. He had explained the consequences of choosing 'the knowledge of good and evil'. But the deed was done anyway! And this one original act has now affected every area of life. As Susan Ashton's song puts it:

Milton lost his paradise
Dorothy lost her way
Vincent lost his sanity
Thomas lost his faith
Hoover lost the second time
Sigmund lost his friend
Me, I lost my innocence
And I want it back again![1]

Is that the end of the story? Surprisingly, no. God goes looking for Adam and Eve and confronts them. They twist and turn a bit, but in essence admit they have done wrong. The Lord then outlines the results of their decision.

God says to the woman, 'I will greatly increase your pains in childbearing; with pain you will give birth to children' (Gen 3:16)

What graciousness! Instead of just throwing the human race away, God shows immediately that he has another plan. He does not say, 'Forget it! So you wanted to have children; well now you've sinned YOU CAN'T!'

No! Instead he says we can start off by going for second best. It will be painful, but you will still bear children. In fact, when you bear children you will be able to get your own back on the serpent, because – eventually – one of your offspring will crush his head (v15); and then the way will be open for every human being to regain the original blessing and enjoy what life was meant to be like.

So Adam and Eve still can have children, even though sin has begun to mess things up.

THE FIRST CHILDREN

If you are not yet sure that the primal reason for the suffering and evil of infertility is the fall (inspired by the devil *not God!*), then look at the effect of sin on Adam and Eve's children.

Cain plants crops, and Abel looks after sheep. It is a very pastoral scene.

But there is poison in the air. Satan knows that it is the Seed of woman that will crush his head. He therefore sets out to destroy, by fair means or foul, the seed of woman. He sets out to make Adam and Eve childless.

The story of Cain and Abel is repeated a million times every week in the modern world. It goes like this . . .

Cain becomes jealous of Abel and kills him. Abel's blood runs into the soil. Cain is discovered, due to the very ground crying out in accusation. So Cain flees from the presence of God, who pronounces: 'When you work the ground, it will no longer yield its crops for you. You will be a restless wanderer on the earth' (Gen 4:12).

Due to Cain's sin the land itself becomes barren. Cain, even though not barren himself – in the sense of childless – experiences what it is like to be barren spiritually and emotionally. The words 'restless wanderer' sum up so much of modern life. Even those with children feel the nagging barrenness of the world that we live in.

Adam and Eve have lost *both* their children. Abel is dead. Cain has gone – off the rails. They are once again childless!

But God's heart is a parent heart. The longing to be a parent is part of the image of God in every adult human being. The cry of the childless – whether children have never been born or, although born, have been sucked down by the destructive torrents of this world – is an unceasing sound in the ears of God. So God *acts!*

In this case he *acts* by giving Adam and Eve another child and therefore establishing a new branch of humanity that will bypass Cain. 'Adam lay with his wife again, and she gave birth to a son and named him Seth, saying, "God has granted me another child in place of Abel, since Cain killed him"' (Gen 4:25).

The name Seth has great significance. It means 'granted'. This is subtly different from 'grace' – which would be a free gift initiated by the giver. This demonstrates that Seth was not 'just born', nor was this something that God did without being asked. Something can only be *granted* if it is specifically *requested*.

Adam and Eve clearly asked God to give them another son, to replace Abel and bypass Cain. God hears the cries of those whose children have been stolen by this sinful world, and – as far as possible – grants their requests! As Jesus said, 'Ask and it will be given to you' (Matt 7:7). It may sound simplistic, but many can testify to the truth of this.

Every miracle is a sign of God's care. Both the Bible and today's world are full of stories of the miracle of giving children to childless couples. **So God cares about childlessness! And God cares about the ache and longing of those experiencing infertility.**

TWO

WHY NOT ME?

*'By faith Abraham, even though he was past age —
and Sarah herself was barren — was enabled to become
a father because he considered him faithful who had
made the promise. And so from this one man, and he
as good as dead, came descendants as numerous as the
stars in the sky and as countless as the sand on the
seashore.'*
(Heb 11:11–12)

*'The promises were spoken to Abraham and to his seed.
The Scripture does not say "and to seeds", meaning many
people, but "and to your seed", meaning one person, who is
Christ.'*
(Gal 3:16)

'Hey, that's great!', we hear you say, 'So God does miracles for people who ask, does he? Well we've asked; and we haven't got anything from God or anyone else! Why hasn't he granted our request?'

You may be surprised to know there are real answers to that question. They fall into these three categories:

1. The devil's spite.
2. Misunderstanding how God's power gets released.
3. God's strategic priorities.

Clues to each of these can be found in the saga of Abraham and Sarah (starting in Genesis 12), the first of many infertile couples who have their story told in the Bible. They are both typical and extraordinary. Typical, because they both pray like mad in private while putting on a brave face in public. Extraordinary, because they are the first of many who were part of God's plan to save the world – through God being born as the man, Jesus!

1. THE DEVIL'S SPITE

The Bible tells us that the devil hates God. It also tells us that God loves people and wants us to love him back. The devil knows that God is too big to attack directly, so hurts God by attacking the people he loves and by doing his best to turn those people away from loving God in return. He has achieved both by leading mankind firstly into sin, and then into the pain and suffering of its consequences. And the pièce de résistance, he then gently breaths the idea into mankind's heart that it is God who gave us the pain and suffering in the first place.

Bitterness and anger towards God are the natural results of suffering. But our anger is being directed at the wrong target.

When it comes to being infertile it is particularly easy to become angry. Even Abraham is recorded to have lashed out with what he thought was justified resentment towards the Lord: 'O Sovereign LORD, what can you give me since I remain childless and the one who will inherit my estate is Eliezer of Damascus?' (Gen 15:2).

But the Lord replies directly and forcefully: 'This man will not be your heir, but a son coming from your own body will be your heir' (15:4).

This tells us that God understood the anger. It also tells us that God is secure enough to handle the fact that infertile people can get angry with him about it, without turning his back on us and saying, 'Forget it! If you can't tell it wasn't my fault then I'm not talking to you!'

This gives me great hope. Childlessness makes people very emotional, so it is essential that God can handle this emotion. Feelings! All sorts of feelings. God understands them.

If you are infertile today you may be feeling like Greg.

Greg [name changed] and his wife had been expecting to have children. They wanted them and had been doing nothing to prevent it happening. Slowly the months passed.

Eventually they went to their GP, got referred to an infertility clinic, and started investigations.

Greg hoped there would be a simple problem that could be solved. He assumed that the problem, when found, would be something to do with his wife's reproductive system. The weeks rolled by and they started their visits to the clinic. Early in the process the doctor asked for a sperm sample. Although this was expected, it still felt threatening and was got over as quickly as possible and then forgotten.

The tension in the house was tangible; Greg was basically happy although worried for his wife – she was really hurting!

It was a mixture of guilt and fear and feelings of letting the side down. It was the worry that the expectations she had for her life were being undermined. But it was also more than that . . . She was worrying about whether her husband would still love her if she was no longer a 'proper woman'. She was scared of being rejected if she was found to be infertile. She was scared of losing what she had – in her husband and her self-respect.

He, on the other hand, was only worried for her. He was being strong and saying, 'Of course I love you; whatever happens!'

Then the doctor called and asked him to visit.

The sperm test had returned and showed an extremely low sperm count. He now had to face the fact that he was the one with the physical problem. He was the one who would have to go in and out of hospital for tests. He was the one who was going to be emotionally weak and needing the support. Everything had turned upside-down! Not surprisingly, he started to feel worried, guilty, depressed and needing reassurance of love.

His wife on the other hand, immediately changed mood and with evident relief became happy again; which did not help him at all!

The tests proceeded. Initially it all looked as if it might be very simple. A little op might cure it.

A few days after coming home from hospital he went back to the clinic. It was bad news. The sperm count was so low it would take a miracle!

The next day he wrote this poem. You may even have written something similar.

> Before I was scared when there was hope,
> Now I am scared there is no hope;
> Where is my hope?
> I cannot feel life, just death
> I cannot feel light, just dark
> I cannot feel full, just empty.
> But somewhere, I feel a sparkle
> A small flame in a lot of darkness.
> But I am consumed in my own sadness.
> I cannot feel for anybody, just everybody.
> How can I reason with life when all I feel is dead?
> I feel as though I'm alone floating through space,
> I feel as though tomorrow there will be . . . less.
> I have never felt so much fear, and confusion.
>   loneliness and anger, emptiness and love.
> I just have to keep remembering my hope.
> I feel as though I've let everybody down.
> Why am I so blind?
>   when your love is all I need.
> I am so sad I cannot trust you,
>   when I know that is all I have . . .
>   . . . to do.[1]

Many of you will understand Greg's feelings.

Isn't it good that God can handle it if you express those feelings!

Ultimately it is the devil who has set things up so that you would remain childless. His aim is to hurt God through making you so bitter and angry that you turn from him. So, make the devil squirm: start talking to God. You may be surprised at his replies.

2. RELEASING GOD'S POWER

God breaks into Abraham's anguished prayer and promises a child. Abraham has faith and somehow the combination of his faith and God's promise move something from a spiritual possibility into being a future certainty.

Faith, faith, faith!

The word faith seems to get thrown around by Christians so easily. But what is it? Why does it work for Abraham, when others feel they believed and believed, and yet are still being disappointed?

Often people looking for healing desperately try to find some 'faith' inside themselves. Others go to meetings led by 'faith healers' or connect up with strange cults. They sometimes end up with stress-related problems on top of the original need for healing. One thing is certain, this is not the kind of faith that Abraham had

> He [God] took him [Abraham] outside and said, 'Look up at the heavens and count the stars – if indeed you can count them.' Then he said to him. 'So shall your offspring be.'
>
> Abram believed the LORD, and he credited it to him as righteousness.
>
> (Gen 15:5–6)

The unique quality in Abraham's faith is that it is in a specific promise from the Lord.

Faith is not summoned up from inside you. Faith is the peaceful trust that you have when you hear God say something to you, and you believe him. For faith to be Abrahamic faith it has to be faith in a specific promise given to *you* by God!

It is not necessarily lack of faith for a modern Christian couple not to be able to conceive or give birth.

Christian faith is not faith in 'faith'. Nor is it faith in things becoming as I would like them. It is trusting that God does have a plan, and that that plan will succeed. It is the faith of a soldier in his or her commanding officer. No one is claiming there will not be a battle. It is just that we are trusting that the plan is so good that we are going to win. We are so convinced of victory that we will do whatever he says, even when we don't understand everything.

There is another scripture that makes the same point:

Against all hope, Abraham in hope believed and so became the father of many nations, just as it had been said to him, 'So shall your offspring be.' Without weakening in his faith, he faced the fact that his body was as good as dead – since he was about a hundred years old – and that Sarah's womb was also dead. Yet he did not waver through unbelief regarding the promise of God, but was strengthened in his faith and gave glory to God, being fully persuaded that God had power to do *what he had promised*. (Rom 4:18–21 our italics)

The key is not our faith, but what God has promised.

So you need to hear a promise before you can have faith in it. No one ever heard God promise them anything, who did not first get to know God, and get used to listening to what he has to say. So we suggest that that is where you start.

Start by making friends with God. He loves you. Start talking to him like you would a friend. Use his name, Jesus. After all friends know each other's names. Talk to him as your father. Tell him what is on your mind. If you are struggling to have children, tell him. If you have someone close who is infertile, ask him to help. Then listen to what he has to say.

If you have never heard God speak to you, you probably have not really understood that it is possible. God made it possible when he came as Jesus. Jesus' death and resurrection opened the way for you to pray to God in Jesus' name and to expect God to connect with you.

As you get to know Jesus you may find he has different priorities to you. You may start talking about infertility, and then he changes the subject to something he puts further up the list. If he does this, trust him! He has your best interest at heart. He also must continue to achieve his purposes throughout the world. Like any good commanding officer he has his strategic priorities.

3. GOD'S STRATEGIC PRIORITIES

Jesus was and is essential for God to achieve his purpose in history. Abraham and Sarah having a child was an essential part of the plan which culminated in Jesus being born to Mary. So, even though God loves every individual person equally, the fact that Abraham's son, Isaac, was born is more important than most!

Some people ask *why* Abraham and Sarah were given a promise by God, while so many other godly couples do not receive the same reassurance or miracle. The most certain answer is that Jesus was going to be the source of millions of miracles. Without Abraham and Sarah's child, the source of all miracles would be cut off. The frontline of the war between God and Satan begins to focus over Sarah having that child. Sarah is infertile. So Sarah must have a miracle. It is important, not just kind.

Throughout Scripture the Lord is seen as developing a strategy to win the world back from the power of sin, pain and the devil. This miracle (like all the others in the Bible) shows all the hallmarks of a tactical move by the Lord. He is cutting across the normal scientific laws that he set up to govern the universe; but he is also setting things up so that he can fulfil his purpose of redeeming the world and making heaven available to all those who truly want to enter.

Even in today's world, when miracles occur, this same pattern emerges. Almost always God seems to act strategically to break the power of doubt, fear, pain and death. His aim is to help people believe that he loves them and that if only they would believe, he will receive them as his children (John 1:12).

God has never chucked miracles about on demand. Everything he does is measured. Nothing is without purpose or a place in his plan!

This may seem discouraging for those reading this who are childless and do not believe they have received a specific promise of a child from God. But look at it another way! Start talking to him about why you are not having children. Maybe it is Satan trying to stop another of God's master strokes from taking place. Then ask God how he wants you to co-operate in releasing power.

Maybe you will receive a promise, a miracle, a breakthrough, and give birth to a child. Maybe your future child has a strategic purpose in God's plan. An awesome responsibility for a parent, but exciting!

But whatever you do, don't start trusting something that God has not said. Don't let your wishful thinking fool you into thinking you have heard a promise when you have not. For to trust anything other than the certain word of God is a recipe for disaster.

ISAAC, JACOB, JOSEPH . . .

It is intriguing to note that in both the next two generations after Abraham there is a recurrence of the temporary infertility problem. Isaac and Rebekah are childless. However, 'Isaac prayed to the LORD on behalf of his wife, because she was barren. The LORD answered his prayer, and his wife Rebekah became pregnant' (Gen 25:21).

When Jacob, one of their sons, marries his second wife, Rachel, it was not quite so easy.

> When Rachel saw that she was not bearing Jacob any children, she became jealous of her sister. So she said to Jacob, 'Give me children, or I'll die!'
>
> Jacob became angry with her and said, 'Am I in the place of God, who has kept you from having children?'
>
> (Gen 30:1,2)

The lovely thing about this row being in the Bible is that it is so up to date. Certainly the experience at the time would not have been pleasant; but it shows us these people are human. Rachel's problem is a very modern one rivalry with her sister – even if it is for the affections of their joint husband! (This is the beginning of the biblical case against polygamy!) Modern problems lead to modern solutions. So, she follows her grandmother-in-law's precedent and decides to use surrogacy! She takes her slave girl and tells Jacob to have children with her! (Gen 30:3ff).

Once again God is not overcome by the sin but deals with the situation as he finds it. He may well not have been pleased with the parents but he does not hold it against the children. So much so that all these children – eventually from four different women – become the fathers of the twelve tribes of Israel – one of the most prestigious titles in history.

However, once again, it is the child of the woman who was initially infertile who is the most significant. 'Then God remembered Rachel; he listened to her and opened her womb. She became pregnant and gave birth to a son and said, "God has taken away my disgrace." She named him Joseph.' (Gen 30:22).

This is the Joseph of technicolour dream-coat fame. Starting off life as the eleventh of twelve sons to a nomadic prince, sold into slavery by his brothers. Then – via prison – eventually ends up as prime minister of Egypt. What a remarkable life!

THREE

WHAT HAVE I DONE WRONG?

I struggled for years thinking I was not worthy to have children, which is the enemy's lie. We even tried to adopt twice. The first baby died before we could adopt. The second time, the mother changed her mind in the middle of her pregnancy. These situations caused a lot of emotional pain, but I said, 'God, I'm going to turn this over to you. I believe you have a special plan for my life, different from any other woman.' Somewhere, I started to understand that God's plan was best.[1]

All this talk of sin can have quite an effect on us. Suffering often leads people to ask the question 'Why?' In particular, people who are infertile often start saying, 'It's all my fault!'

Even though this is really a very unhelpful way of thinking, it is important that we deal with what the Bible teaches in this area, rather than ignore it. Only then can this thinking be changed permanently.

The Bible has two things to say about this:

1. Yes! There is a **direct link** between sin and bad things happening.
2. But! Once you become a Christian, punishment is **no longer the point.** After all, Jesus has paid for all our sin. The only 'point' is to overcome the effects of sin.

The direct link between sin and suffering is outlined in a number of passages in the Old Testament. There is then another direct link between getting right with God and things going well. In particular it mentions the matter of childlessness.

> If you pay attention to these laws and are careful to follow them, then the LORD your God will keep his covenant of love with you, as he swore to your forefathers. . . . You will be blessed more than any other people; none of your men or women will be childless, nor any of your livestock without young.
>
> (Deut 7:12,14)

The key to solving any problem is knowing the cause. The inference of the passage of Scripture above is that the reason that we have problems in this life is that we have worshipped other gods, not listened to the prophets the Lord has sent, and failed to obey the Lord when he has spoken! And, listed among the basic areas of human life that will be affected, are miscarriages, barrenness and childlessness!

Our difficulty right now is that some of you reading this are saying, 'But I do worship God! I do listen to what he says and try to obey him! So why am I infertile?'

It is a good question, and one that deserves a detailed answer. There are three points the Bible makes about this Old Testament cause-and-effect teaching:

1. It is designed to give **information not condemnation**
2. It is about a **nation/group of people not an individual**
3. It is *part* of **God's progressive revelation**, and should not be read in isolation from the New Testament.

INFORMATION not CONDEMNATION

This piece of history is in the Bible in order to teach us, rather than condemn us.

In 1 Corinthians 10 verse 6, talking about various Old Testament narratives, it says: 'Now these things occurred as examples to keep us from setting our hearts on evil things as they did.'

And again in verses 11 and 12 of the same chapter: 'These things happened to them as examples and were written down as warnings for us, on whom the fulfilment of the ages has come. So, if you think you are standing firm, be careful that you don't fall!'

And again, put rather more positively, in Romans 15 verse 4: 'For everything that was written in the past was written to teach us, so that through endurance and the encouragement of the Scriptures we might have hope.'

The point of us knowing the stories of the Israelites is that we who live in this age might understand how the spiritual world works and would have no excuse for ignorance of the way all the blessings and cursings of God's world function.[2]

The law never sounds 'nice!'. Even though most of us agree that it is sensible, it makes us squirm. Why? Because, if we are honest, we know we do not live up to its requirements.

However, we must not be afraid of it! The law was given to help us. You see it is only as we are aware of what God's original plan was, and why things do not happen that way anymore, that we can start to do something about making ourselves available to be part of the solution.

As the Bible says, 'The law was our schoolmaster to bring us unto Christ, that we might be justified by faith' (Gal 3:24, AV).

It's like this . . .

When my sister, Sarah, was still a small child, my family lived in Bahrain – where my father was serving as a naval officer. The water was not very pleasant and as a result, our thirst was quenched with various fizzy drinks – Coke and lemonade being the most popular.

The problem with this practice was that Sarah's teeth rotted. As a four-year-old she did not swallow the corrosive liquid and soon the dentist was having fun trying to rebuild her chompers. There was great anguish in the household and pain in her mouth. But that was not the end of the story.

As most people know, a human being is given two chances with teeth. Soon after we are born we get our 'milk teeth'. At seven or so we lose these – sometimes leaving them under our pillows in the hope of getting money! – and then they are replaced by an adult set. Any damage done to the first lot is lost, removed and given a rightful place in family history. And the eating capacity returns to 100 per cent.

By the time Sarah was an adult she had a perfectly good set of teeth!

Now this story, like the history of Israel in the Scriptures, can act as a parable with either of two effects.

Firstly, as a cautionary tale. Small children could be reminded again and again of the terrible fate of teeth regularly soaked in Coca Cola. The story could be told graphically with shouts of pain and visuals of dentist's chairs, so that any small conscience that even glanced up the soft drink aisle in the supermarket would be consumed with guilt.

On the other hand, it is a story of the magnificent creative ability of God. It is a fact that God took into account that as children we might mess up and, due to the foolishness of consuming too much sugar-laden liquid, might rot our teeth. He therefore went out of his way to design an automatically-installed replacement set. It is too marvellous, for words. Of course this never suggests that allowing your teeth to perish is a good idea! What's more, once you have the second set you must now be careful to look after them! But the emphasis is on the glory of the provision. The story leads us to a place of praising God for his grace.

This second approach is the right way of reading the epics and laws of the Old Testament. Only when we realise what a dreadful situation humanity had caused by choosing to ignore God, can we truly appreciate the wonder and glory of his redemption plan in Jesus.

2. GROUP NOT INDIVIDUAL

The Lord is speaking to a whole nation, not a single person/ couple.

Even if you as an individual have got right with God – by trusting in Jesus' sacrifice and resurrection – you may still be living in a nation and world that is experiencing the withdrawal of God's hand – i.e. judgement – because of the way it is behaving. This would free the devil to continue to

wreak havoc in your physical life. We need to do more
than just turn to the Lord individually to experience heaven
on earth. We need instead to bring our whole churches,
towns, nations and world into God's Kingdom. Then our
'light will break forth like the dawn, and [our] healing
quickly appear; then [our] righteousness will go before
[us], and the glory of the Lord will be [our] rear guard'
(Is 58:8).

3. ONLY PART OF GOD'S REVELATION

All this Old Testament material has to be read in the context
of what Jesus would do and say, not in isolation.

It is very easy from the way many religious leaders
seem to use the Bible, to get the idea that if there is one
verse that backs up their point of view, then that view is
indisputable. Christians have always understood the Bible
to be a **progressive revelation**. So it is only as we read
each verse in the context of the complete Bible that we
shall understand how we should apply it. And the key to
understanding the whole Bible is Jesus (Matt 5:17).

The Old Testament is the backdrop, but the real action
takes place in the New. Jesus becomes centre stage! Now
we begin to see God's plan. He intends to break the power of
sin. He also intends to turn every curse that Satan or sin has
caused. Through the cross, resurrection and present power
of Jesus, the Holy Spirit is given to the believer. We are
then meant to co-operate with the Lord by:

either breaking the power of evil, pain and suffering by
praying in Jesus' name and seeing each curse destroyed.
So if people are sick, they get well; imprisoned, set free;
doubting, they believe; infertile, they get married and have
children!

or – equally amazing – allowing the Holy Spirit to lead
us to see that a particular area of suffering in our lives
(e.g. infertility), although it had its source in evil, can now
become for us a gateway to a new destiny. As we love and
trust the Lord, he will take that which was meant for our
evil, and turn it for our good (Rom 8:28; Gen 50:20).

This is not to say that this 'new destiny' can ever replace having biological children. But the blessing you get from it is not one you would have been able to enjoy if you had not suffered infertility first.

So now, the issue of 'Am I being punished?', is no longer the point. The focus of your life comes off the 'whys' of my sin, your sin, or even Adam and Eve's sin.

Instead of looking backwards, asking who's fault it all is; now your life looks forward, taking each day as a challenge, and each problem as an opportunity to overcome in Jesus' name.

FOUR

AS JESUS SAID

> *. . . let not any eunuch complain,*
> *'I am only a dry tree.'*
> *For this is what the LORD says:*
> *'To the eunuchs who keep my Sabbaths,*
> *who choose what pleases me*
> *and hold fast to my covenant—*
> *to them I will give within my temple and its walls*
> *a memorial and a name*
> *better than sons and daughters;*
> *I will give them an everlasting name*
> *that will not be cut off'*
> *(Is 56:3–5)*

Jesus had a great deal to say about children! He is very positive about both their value to God, and the power of their example to those of us longer in the tooth. For example:

'I tell you the truth, unless you change and become like little children, you will never enter the kingdom of heaven. Therefore, whoever humbles himself like this child is the greatest in the kingdom of heaven.

'And whoever welcomes a little child like this in my name welcomes me. But if anyone causes one of these little ones who believe in me to sin, it would be better for him to have a large millstone hung around his neck and to be drowned in the depths of the sea.'

(Matt 18:3–6)

Jesus obviously loves children, even though he never humanly fathered any himself. Jesus loves children, and he also speaks passionately about being childless in this world.

At a first reading it may appear to be one of his asides. But at closer inspection you will discover this is not the case.

> Jesus replied, 'Not everyone can accept this word, but only those to whom it has been given. For some are eunuchs because they were born that way; others were made that way by men; and others have renounced marriage because of the kingdom of heaven. The one who can accept this should accept it.'
>
> (Matt 19:11–12)

The main subject of this passage is the ethics of divorce and remarriage. Some may think that because of the phrase 'have renounced marriage' (v12) that it is wrong to use this verse to explore Jesus' thoughts and feelings about infertility. We beg to differ for three reasons.

1. Eunuch means infertile man.
2. 'Renounced marriage' is better translated 'made themselves eunuchs'.
3. Giving up things or desired family relationships is referred to in other places in the Bible as normal for those who wish to follow Jesus (e.g. Matt 19:29).

So Jesus is talking here about the various reasons a person will be without children. He gives three:

1. because they were born that way;
2. because they were made that way by men;
3. because they have chosen that way because of the kingdom of heaven.

1. BORN THAT WAY

Some people are born infertile. Others are born in such a way to never get married. For the former it may be something to do with a fault in their biology, or else some sickness or disease that has damaged them. For the latter, there are various reasons. Many single people would prefer to stay single; others long to find someone with whom they can 'get together', but in this complex world they never seem to come along. And, particularly as a Christian, if you cannot find a husband/wife, you cannot have children.

The situation begs the question 'Why?'

Some would like to blame God. They ask, 'How could a God who is all-powerful and loving not only make some people biologically infertile, but also make a society that does not have the right combination of people for each to have a partner?' The question is valid.

Of course our all-powerful, loving God did not set out to make people with faults or a world so evil and self-destructive as the one we live in. Nor did he do so. At the beginning, having made the universe, he said, 'It is very good!' And it was!

The problem came with sin. Although, in his mercy, God slowed the rot that sin caused, he still left us in a world that had some good and some evil.

So we now live in a beautiful world that God made 'very good'; but which also continues to show the cracks of evil in sickness, imbalance, injustice, doubt, fear and 'some being born eunuchs'. This was not God's original blueprint. He would have known it would happen, but it is not what he intended.

What now? Is there any hope of healing this condition.

Obviously now we are speaking specifically about 'healing' of those born infertile. The broader definition of 'being born a eunuch' discussed above includes issues that need healing of a different order.

We think there are four possibilities:

a. Some can be 'healed' by doctors as they mobilise what God has provided.

b. Some can be 'healed' by God directly when they either pray or are prayed for.

c. Some have another destiny (see number 3)

d. Some are part of the struggle of this sinful perishing world that, although the salvation bought by God

in Christ has released some of the good and the
healing back into it, is never – before the Second
Coming of Christ – going to see everyone completely whole.

It is this fourth group that we are most concerned
about. You feel that you were made to have children.
But, no matter what you do, it is not going to happen. You've tried the doctors. You've prayed and been
prayed for. You would love to find something else to fulfil
your heart. But nothing seems to break into that yawning
gap inside.

But you do believe in God. You do believe in Jesus. So
why doesn't the way you are motivated connect with what
you can actually do?

The answers are simple, but not easy. Until Jesus comes
again this world will not be as it is meant to be. 'Now we
see dimly like in a dirty mirror; then face to face' (1 Cor
13:12 our paraphrase).

Our suggestion, if you are in this position, is to read Job.
It is a strange story of a conversation between a good man
who is suffering and a few pious friends.

Job's advisors kept telling him his troubles were caused
by sin in his life. But he knew this was not the case. He knew
that his Redeemer was alive, even though it was not making
any difference at a practical level. So, for no other apparent
reason than that God existed and was good, Job, through
gritted teeth, praised him! And the glory of the story is that
that changed everything!!

Habakkuk put it like this:

Though the fig-tree does not bud
    and there are no grapes on the vines,
though the olive crop fails
    and the fields produce no food,
though there are no sheep in the pen
    and no cattle in the stalls,
yet I will rejoice in the LORD,
    I will be joyful in God my Saviour.

(Hab 3:17,18)

2. MEN MADE THEM THAT WAY

A few years ago, the infertility statistics for the UK were 1 in 10. In the 1980s the figure became 1 in 7. Doctors are now telling us that the number is rising still further and will soon be 1 in 6. Why this increase? We cannot blame the same cause that Jesus had in mind. After all he was probably referring to various conquering armies which, in those days, had the habit of making men eunuchs in order to use them as slaves who could look after their harems. The method was castration. Today's causes may turn out to be a little more subtle.

Studies have been carried out recently suggesting that stress, pace of life, divorce, fashion, pollution (particularly of oestrogen-like chemicals), overpopulation, alcohol, smoking, contraception, or a number of other modern phenomena may have caused infertility as a side-effect. There seems to be some truth in these speculations.

Other human causes could be:

- A surgeon who damages you during an operation.
- An overdose of drugs you took.
- Sexual abuse while you were a child, or later.
- Falling from a tree, car crash or other accident.
- Malnourishment – particularly for people in the Two-Thirds World.
- A sports injury.
- Injury due to having an abortion.
- Being sexually promiscuous.
- think of another . . .

The problem is that each person who is infertile 'because men made them that way' has **got someone to blame.**

In number 1 (above) the only course of action is look to God and praise him. In number 3 (below) you will discover that there is an element of choice. But here, number 2, it is someone's *fault!* So, if you want to, it is possible to do something.

Here are some of the possible somethings you could do:

a. Forgive them! and let it go . . . (if it is someone else's fault).
b. Forgive yourself! (if it is maybe your fault).
c. Sue them!
d. Sue them! then forgive them!
e. Through letter or lobbying, persuade them to change policy.
f. Through direct peaceful action, persuade them . . . etc.
g. Provide/raise finance for a group working in that area.
h. Organise something to undo the damage caused (e.g., pollution).
i. Start a support group for folk who have been through something similar.
j. Start a prayer cell to put the problem before the Lord.

We do *not* suggest that you track down the culprit and do them some injury! Two wrongs do not make a right. We must become part of the solution, not perpetuate problems.

The key issue is forgiveness. No matter what other action you take, your relationship with God will depend on it. As it says in the Lord's Prayer: 'Forgive us our sins, as we forgive those who sin against us.'

Forgiveness is still misunderstood. If someone has really done something wrong, then that sin should be punished. Forgiving someone is not telling God that he should not punish them. Forgiveness is just telling God it is his business what he does with them, not ours! It is the choice not to spend my life being angry, bitter and vengeful. Instead I will release this person into God's hand. If God sees fit to judge them, that's his business. If he should forgive them – because they claim the blood of Christ – that's also his business.

But our responsibilities do not stop with forgiveness. What if this person or company's actions might lead to other innocent people suffering? In this case we should also let the relevant authorities know. In this case revenge is not the purpose. We are simply trying our best to co-operate with the Lord in getting his justice and order established on the earth.

We believe the causes of our infertility fall into this category.

As I said in the Introduction, I had an operation as a teenager to remove cysts on my ovaries. Afterwards there were some complications. The doctors found it very difficult to talk to my parents. It was all a bit suspicious.

Later, when I was married, I asked the doctor to send for the notes of the operation to see if there might be some reason why I might find having children difficult. Strangely all the notes had been 'lost'.

Of course, we are not accusing anybody. But it is strange!

This has made me angry. Not so much that they may have made a mistake. More that there is a strange silence. It would at least have been useful to know what happened. Then I could have made plans; not to sue them – just to forgive them. Of course!

3. CHOSE THAT WAY BECAUSE OF THE KINGDOM OF HEAVEN

There are three ways to make this choice:

a. Responding to the call to celibacy and therefore having no children.

b. Getting married but also receiving and responding to a call from God not to have children. These couples will not ever be sure they are fertile. (You can only be sure by experimentation!)

c. Getting married and expecting to reproduce, but discovering you cannot have children. In this state of infertility, you cry out to God for reasons, then hearing and responding to a call from God to some other work that you could/would not have done with children. This may never compensate for having children, but may explain the reason why you as a couple faced this particular problem.

The key to each of the above is that it must be a call from God. Just responding to circumstances will never bring you to the same kind of peace as hearing from God that it all makes sense.

A similar situation to this was illustrated by a story a friend of ours shared with us.

She was an incorrigible matchmaker. Whenever she saw an eligible single person she started trying to work out who they would 'fit' with. One of her friends was extremely resistant to being paired up and she teased him mercilessly.

One evening, when they had not seen each other for a while, they met at a concert. The usual banter started with her saying, 'Where are we going to find you a wife?' when suddenly she stopped.

'It was as if I saw a shining robe all around him. It was glorious, and I knew God was showing me something. Even as I looked, I knew that it was celibacy, and I seemed to hear a voice. It was God's voice, and he was telling me not to touch. He would have been very angry if I had gone on!'

She told us that it certainly tempered, if not quite cured, her matchmaking habit.

The Holy Spirit also inspired Paul to write about this:

What I mean, brothers, is that the time is short. From now on those who have wives should live as if they had none; those who mourn, as if they did not; those who are happy, as if they were not; those who buy something, as if it were not theirs to keep; those who use the things of the world, as if not engrossed in them. For this world in its present form is passing away.

I would like you to be free from concern. An unmarried man is concerned about the Lord's affairs – how he can please the Lord. But a married man is concerned about the affairs of this world – how he can please his wife – and his interests are divided. An unmarried woman or virgin is concerned about the Lord's affairs: Her aim is to be devoted to the Lord in both body and spirit. But a married woman is concerned about the affairs of this world – how she can please her husband. I am saying this for your own good, not to restrict you, but that you may live in a right way in undivided devotion to the Lord.

(1 Cor 7:29–35)

These 'glorious mantles' both of celibacy and – we believe
– childlessness, do exist. Other people, even members of the
Christian church, do not necessarily understand. But in this
gospel age it is regularly necessary for Christians to make
this kind of sacrifice in order that 'the lamb who was slain
might receive the reward of his suffering'.

It may seem a 'hard teaching', but this is certainly
not unique among Jesus' teaching. For all his peace and
gentleness, Father God retains a hard-headed approach
to breaking the back of the evil in this world. It may be
invisible, but there is a war on! And the key to winning
wars is people, of their own free will, making sacrifices.

So this is written with the same spirit of love and longing.
Longing that you, we and everybody else should be happy
and fulfilled. But also longing that we should see that the
key to eternal fulfilment and happiness is never to be
found in this world. And therefore longing that we should
not shrink back into middle-class mediocrity. But instead,
married or not, with children or not, that we should press
on to the goal, laying down the love of our lives, and taking
hold of that for which Christ took hold of us (Phil 3:12).

FIVE

THE MEDICAL MAZE

In the western world, both those with a Christian faith and those without are as likely to expect God to provide a miracle through the medical profession as from a prayer meeting. In this and the next chapter we want to explore the methods and morals of these two very different routes to 'healing' infertility. Both are a minefield, so let's start with the simpler one first: the medical maze.

Infertility clinics across the UK have not yet established a standard set of guidelines. Each area has a slightly different way of doing things. This, however, should not to be a problem at this book's level of competence. For those who know the complexities of medical techniques used in infertility treatment, this chapter will seem shallow. But as our aim is to cater for ordinary folk who simply want information regarding the normal pattern of events, we feel this is sufficient. Knowledge will not necessarily change the treatment you receive, but it may reduce the stress or fear experienced when approaching the time of an appointment.

One other thing. The style of writing in this chapter is slightly different from the previous chapters. The nature of medical facts is that they have to be approached analytically. It is not so much about feelings as about objects that are or are not in the right place. Do not be put off by this. If it seems too much in one go, then jump forward to the next chapter. You can then go back and use this material more as a reference book. However, if you want to get the big picture of all that could happen, this is a rough outline.

So let us start at the beginning:

GETTING INTO THE SYSTEM

The first thing that is likely to happen is that you will get married – although this step may get left out if you are not yet a Christian – and you will begin to make love regularly. You may use some form of contraception for a while after marriage. Then, when both of you are ready to have children you may start to have 'unprotected' sex.

If you are already worried that you might be infertile you may well have had check-ups or talked it through with your GP, although this is not usual. Most GPs will chat about anything to anybody, but it is not usual to refer someone for further investigation unless the need is immediate.

It is important to make a note of when you start trying for a baby. The reason for this is that normal policy is not to define a couple as infertile until they have been having unfruitful unprotected sex for at least 12 months. This time varies between regions so it is worth asking your GP about the local policy. It is normal for specialists to refuse to see people before this stage.

It is also worth noting that the medical profession prefer to define this stage as 'subfertile', rather than 'infertile', as many couples who seek help will subsequently go on to achieve a pregnancy. (However, for simplicity we shall go on using the term 'infertile'.)

Once your GP is satisfied you fit this category, he/she will set up an appointment which is normally within the next few weeks. Don't panic! Ten to fifteen per cent of all couples trying to conceive will not have done so within one year. You are not alone! What's more, only 5–7 per cent will still not have conceived within two years. Therefore, having reached 12 months of trying unsuccessfully, just by going on trying for another year, you have a

50 per cent chance of the biology coming together all by itself!

POSSIBLE CAUSES OF INFERTILITY

It is estimated – in present research – that of all couples seeking help for infertility, the causes are:

Female factors	35%
Male factors	30%
A combination	20%
Unknown	15%

About 40 per cent of the 'no cause found' group will achieve pregnancy within two years.

Age can also be a factor. The age of maximum female fertility is 24 years, and then it steadily declines. Over 40 years of age, the pregnancy rate falls significantly and the miscarriage rate increases.

On the male side it is less clear. We have not been able to obtain any information regarding trends of lesser or greater male fertility or infertility in relation to age.

HOW IS IT MEANT TO WORK?

Sperm is produced in the male testicles (see fig 1), ejaculated into the female vagina (fig 2 A) and has to pass through the cervix (fig 2 B), uterus (fig 2 C) and into the fallopian tube (fig 2 D). At the same time an ovum needs to have been ovulated from the ovary (fig 2 E), and have started to travel down the fallopian tube. The sperm must meet with an ovum and then fertilise it. The fertilised egg must then pass down the fallopian tube and inbed in the uterine lining. If any stage of this is hindered or blocked then infertility can result.

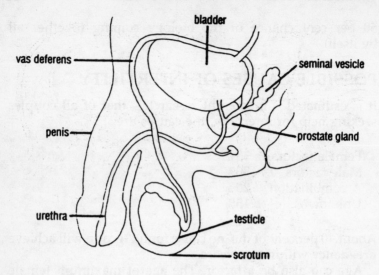

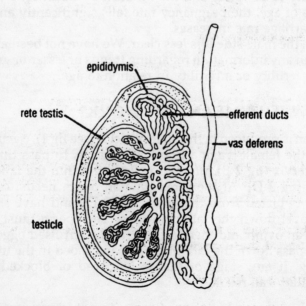

The male reproductive system.

Figure 1   Male Sexual Organs

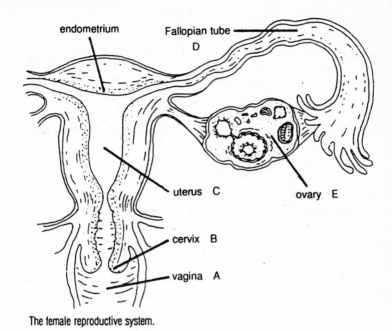

The female reproductive system.

Figure 2   Female Sexual Organs

WHAT MIGHT BE THE PROBLEM?

This next section by its very nature will be quite technical.

If you are more interested in general themes than details about testes and Fallopian tubes, then skip through the next pages picking up the text when it moves out of note form. Later, if you need more detail you can always come back.

Where there is a physical cause to be found it will fall into one of these categories:

a) Failure of Ovulation

i.e. The woman is not producing (or not producing effectively) the ovum (which is the proper word for what most of us call the egg).

POSSIBLE REASONS:

- Hormonal Problems

    The female body has at least four parts that secrete chemicals (hormones) which send a message to the reproductive organs to go on to the next stage of the monthly or reproductive cycle. The four are **the ovary** itself, **the hypothalamus** (in the brain), **the pituitary gland** (at the base of the brain) and **the thyroid gland** (in the neck). If any of these is malfunctioning it can cause problems with ovulation.

    The symptoms for hormonal problems may include: infrequent or non-existent periods; weight gain, new or excessive body and/or facial hair. It must be noted that excessive weight loss can be a cause for fertility problems.

- Scarred Ovaries

    This can be caused by repeated infections in the pelvic area and/or surgery to the ovaries themselves, e.g. for the removal of ovarian cysts. It can also be a side-effect of pelvic radiation therapy for cancer.

- Premature Menopause

    This is uncommon, but consists of a woman stopping producing eggs and also stopping having periods. Other symptoms include hot flushes and/or dry vagina. (However these symptoms are quite common among women and do not necessarily mean that the 'change of life' has come.)

- Follicle Problems

    This is the area – like a blister – on the ovary in which the ovum develops. Sometimes, for little understood reasons, one or more of these will fail to rupture, and therefore will trap the ovum. There are no specific symptoms for this that anyone has clearly isolated.

- Psychological Reasons

    It is quite *normal* for every woman at some time in her life not to ovulate for one or more months. This is usually to do with some particularly stressful situation e.g. exams, loss of job, bereavement, or marital break-up. It is unusual for this to have a prolonged effect. Statistically the facts are against the popular myths of psychological factors playing a major role in causing infertility.

b) Failure of the Fallopian Tubes

i.e. Some damage or blocking to the tubes down which the ovum must travel (or be propelled) to both meet the sperm and reach the uterus.

POSSIBLE REASONS
- Inflammation (*salpingitis*)
  This may be associated with infection, abdominal disease or may follow childbirth, miscarriage or abortion. Various micro-organisms can cause tubal scarring and other damage. It is possible to catch these infections through sexual intercourse (VD etc) but according to a recent study only about 10 per cent of infection could be tracked to this source.[1] Other causes can be appendicitis, peritonitis or colitis (all of which can spread from other organs in the abdomen).

- Surgical Damage
  This is common among women who have had previous surgery in the abdomen, pelvic area, uterus, ovaries or Fallopian tubes. Particularly, before they used microscopes for this surgery, it was possible to leave adhesions that 'glued' the tubes down and made it impossible or difficult for the eggs to travel through them.

- Ectopic Pregnancy
  If a previous pregnancy has taken place in the Fallopian tube – which is not meant to happen – this can cause damage/scarring. Even more importantly, if you have damage/scarring in your tube it can induce an ectopic pregnancy, which can be life-threatening.

- **Congenital Defect**
  This is the medical term for saying that some women are just born with an abnormality.

- **Endometriosis**
  This is a condition where the lining of the uterus also starts to grow inside the Fallopian tubes (and sometimes even right through them and out round the ovaries and part of the abdominal lining). Occasionally it can lead to severe scarring or adhesions.

c) An Abnormal Uterus

i.e. Some defect that either stops the build up/discarding of the uterus lining in the monthly cycle. Or else something that stops either the sperm passing through the uterus or the fertilsed egg from implanting itself in the uterine wall. Ten per cent of all female infertility is caused by a problem in this area.

POSSIBLE REASONS
- **Fibroids**
  These are very common (1 in 3 women have them). They are benign (non-cancerous) tumours that grow in almost any part of the uterus. Many women have them and stay completely fertile. It seems to be only when they grow somewhere where they cause a blockage that they cause a problem.
  Symptoms include increasingly heavy and painful periods and/or swelling in the abdomen.

- **Adenomyosis**
  Similar to endometriosis (above) this is when the uterine lining begins to form around areas for which it was not intended. In this case it is in the thick muscle of the uterus.
  It can cause prolonged painful periods and a dull pain can set in, particularly during intercourse. Occasionally the uterus may be enlarged and a bit tender.

- **Congenital Abnormalities**
  As with the Fallopian tubes, many women are born

with a uterus which has a difficulty. The most common is called a *septate uterus*. During the formation of the human uterus two tubes come together and make one whole. Sometimes this process occurs without the membrane in the middle completely disappearing. Although this obstructs the uterus it does not normally stop conception, but instead can cause repeated miscarriage.

- Uterine Adhesions

  Again, as for the Fallopian tubes, it is possible – and very common – for women who have experienced some scarring to the uterus wall to find bits of the wall get 'stuck' together. The scarring is regularly caused by a traumatic previous pregnancy, or a curettage ('scrape' or 'D and C') after a miscarriage or abortion. If you have had one of these and your periods have become painful and irregular or stopped completely, this could be the difficulty.

- Foreign Body in the Uterus

  Anything solid in the uterus can cause enough irritation to stop a fertilised egg from attaching – or staying attached – to the uterine lining. Objects can be man-made and introduced from outside (this is how the contraceptive coil works – aborting a fertilised egg), or can grow inside like fibroids or polyps (fleshy, grape-like growths of uterine lining that are not shed during periods).

d) Failure of Sperm Transportation through the Cervix

POSSIBLE REASONS
- Problems with the Cervix

  There are two possible problems here:

  1) After intercourse the sperm that has been ejaculated should stay in the mucus of the cervix, which acts like a reservoir out of which the sperm will swim into the

uterus and on. If the sperm does not survive in the cervical mucus (for any reason, normally relating to hormonal imbalance) then they will not be able to continue their journey.

2) Once pregnancy occurs, the cervix should shut and seal the uterus. If this does not happen properly, the membrane can get infected, rupture and induce miscarriage. This is quite common and is the normal cause of a miscarriage at about 16–26 weeks. However it is quite easy to treat by putting in a stitch to keep the cervix shut!

• Abnormalities in the Sperm Production

This may be because there is **no sperm** in the semen. Reasons for this can include a difficulty that the man is born with (genetic), a failure of the testicles dropping, hormonal problems, a blockage in the tubes that move the sperm out of the testicles or (in about 1 per cent of cases) a syndrome called *retrograde ejaculation* which means that the genital muscles are not working properly and the sperm is going to the bladder instead of out through the penis.

Alternatively it could be because there are **few sperm** in the semen. Low sperm count is the normal (70 per cent) diagnosis of those suffering male infertility. Assuming the sperm are healthy it is something that can almost certainly be overcome.

The bigger problem is a **low sperm count where the sperm are largely abnormal or of low motility** (i.e. mobility). This can be as a result of a genetic defect; hormonal or immunological difficulties, caused by abnormal blood vessels around the testicles, in turn caused by an infection (e.g. mumps) or even by the lifestyle/environment of the man concerned. For example: smoking, alcohol, excessive exercise, being overweight, occupational hazards (e.g., long-distance driving, exposure to poisonous substances, etc), caffeine, drugs or the stresses of work/daily life are all thought to play a part in the health of a man's sperm. Some even say that wearing boxer shorts is better than Y-fronts – which we all know are a little restrictive!

• Abnormalities of ejaculation
This includes all problems relating to sexual inter-course, both physical and psychological.
Anatomical abnormalities can include the inability to get an erection, or a condition known as *hypospadias*, when the tube that carries the sperm comes out of the penis at its base. Both of these physical problems can be cured.
Psychological issues are more complex but also very common both among Christians and non-Christians. If you are married or preparing for marriage and struggling with the issues of making love, may we suggest you contact 'CARE for the Family' and ask them to put you in touch with a counsellor trained in marriage guidance. This can be embarrassing to you, but those you contact will be used to discussing these issues.

WHAT DO THE DOCTORS DO?

Once a couple have been referred to a specialist the process falls into three distinct areas:

a) ASSESSMENT
b) ADVICE AND INVESTIGATION
c) TREATMENT

We will deal with them in order.

a) Assessment

The ideal initial assessment is to see both partners, take a full history and to examine both of them. A lot of questions may seem unnecessarily intrusive but it is very common in the population at large for people to have had multiple partners (and maybe other pregnancies) or to have had sexually-transmitted diseases. The more information to hand initially, the easier it is to direct the appropriate investigations in order to establish the cause of the problem.

The questions asked should cover these kinds of areas:

Female History:
- age
- delay in conception – *duration, investigations so far, effect on life*
- menstrual history – *age of onset of periods, cycles, features suggesting ovulation such as mucus change, midcycle pain, menstrual symptoms*
- reproductive history – *previous pregnancies*
- past contraception
- past medical history – *especially pelvic infection, abdominal or pelvic surgery*
- recent weight change
- medication
- alcohol, smoking, etc
- occupation
- psychological or previous psychiatric history

Female Examination:
Height, weight, blood pressure, evidence of a 'hormonal' problem (e.g. thyroid problem), rubella, and a full vaginal examination.

Male History:
- age
- sexual history – *puberty, erection, ejaculation*
- reproductive history – *past pregnancies fathered*
- past medical history – *especially testicular torsion (twisting) or maldescent (failure to drop), trauma to genitalia, mumps, chronic illness, radiation exposure, sexually transmitted diseases*
- medication
- occupation

- smoking, alcohol, etc
- psychological factors

Male Examination:
Height, weight, blood pressure, and examination of the genitalia

b) Advice and Investigation

Assuming that more than 12 months of 'unprotected' intercourse has elapsed, and depending on the findings from the history and examination, the following initial investigations and advice would be initiated (probably by the GP but maybe by an infertility clinic):

i)   General advice regarding smoking, alcohol, weight, reducing testicular temperature (*no hot baths, wear boxer shorts!*) and coital timing (i.e., when to have sex so that it matches with the woman's most fertile time of the month). Theoretically ovulation will occur approximately 14 days before the period starts; if a woman has a 35-day cycle, then she will ovulate on approximately day 21.

ii) Normal advice given to any woman before trying to conceive, such as diet, folic acid supplements and checking for rubella antibodies.

iii) Semen analysis, twice, one month apart. This should be checked in every couple seeking help. The man must abstain from intercourse or ejaculation for two to three days prior to collecting the sample. He must masturbate into a wide-mouthed container and transport the specimen at body temperature to the laboratory within one to two hours. The laboratory looks at the volume of the ejaculate, the total sperm count and the motility of the sperm, together with the number of abnormal forms. The average man ejaculates between 100 million and 300 million sperm. It is quite likely that some reading the above paragraph will find themselves worried by some of the ideas about masturbation and the all-too-clinical approach to the issue. Some men

particularly feel embarrassed by the whole procedure –
maybe even most men. But please note, the couple can
quite easily achieve the ejaculation together and in the
privacy of their own home. These fictional TV movies
where a man is stuck in the doctor's waiting-room
toilet with a few magazines are scare stories and very
unhelpful!

iv)   If the woman is having periods fairly regularly (up
      to every six weeks) then a basal body temperature
      chart can be helpful in assessing whether or not she
      is ovulating. Typically, in the first half of the cycle
      the basal temperature is low, and on the day before
      ovulation there is a drop in the temperature of 0.5°C,
      then a rise above the previous baseline for two to four
      days and a subsequent levelling off. The temperature
      needs to be recorded on a special thermometer which
      can be bought in a chemist or prescribed by the GP.
      The temperature must be taken immediately upon
      waking and after five hours of uninterrupted sleep
      – it therefore is sometimes impractical! A blood test
      in the second half of the cycle (seven days before the
      period is due) can also help establish whether or not
      ovulation is occurring.

v)   If the woman is having only infrequent periods, if any
      at all, then a blood test is arranged to look at her
      hormone profile and thyroid function.

The GP or clinic may wish to refer you to the local hospital
(or in some regions they have the responsibility to do
this themselves) for further investigations or treatment of
problems discovered during these initial investigations.
   Five basic tests will establish the cause of subfertility
in 80–90 per cent of couples. Three of these have been
outlined above, namely, basal temperature charts, blood
tests to check on the presence of ovulation and semen
analysis. The other two tests are:

i)   Postcoital Test – this is performed just before the
      expected time of ovulation. The couple are asked to
      have intercourse prior to being seen (the night before is

acceptable) and a sample of the cervical mucus is taken from the woman. The latter is not unlike having a smear test done. The quality of the mucus is assessed, along with the mobility and numbers of the sperm present.

ii) Tests of Tubal Patency – laparoscopy with hydro-tubatiokn is the usual procedure. Those in the know call it the 'lap and dye test'. This is performed under general anaesthetic and a fibre-optic television camera is used to look into the abdomen and pelvis. Dye is used to assess whether the Fallopian tubes are working properly. (This can be done using X-rays but it is not so effective.) Recently a new way of testing in this area has been developed using a fibre-optic camera sent into the woman's tubes via her cervix and uterus, but this is not yet universally available.

Other possible investigations include ultrasound of the ovaries (which can help to detect cysts on the ovaries, and even the ovulation itself), male hormonal blood tests if there is a very low or zero sperm count and, rarely, a testicular biopsy (cutting out a piece to have a look at it!), if there is difficulty in deciding if a low sperm count is due to low production or a blockage in the man's tubes.

Treatment Options

Given time, many couples will conceive naturally, but there are various strategies for helping, depending on the cause of the problem.

i) Problems in Ovulation

Treatment of failure to ovulate consists of, firstly, correcting any weight loss, obesity, thyroid problem or other medical conditions. If this is unsuccessful, clomiphene is the most commonly-used drug. It works by altering the feedback mechanism of the hormones on the brain which causes a large release of the body's own ovarian stimulating hormone. Ovulation is produced in approximately 72 per cent of women with this. There is, however, a sixfold increase in multiple pregnancy in women who have taken clomiphene

– the majority are twins. If this fails, stimulating hormones are given direct, rather than relying on the woman's own supply.

ii) Tubal Problems

Tubal surgery yields variable results depending on the expertise of the surgeon and the severity of the tubal problem. About 40 per cent of patients undergoing microsurgery can go on to give birth. Tubal reimplantations are less successful, with pregnancy rates of 11 per cent. Reversal of sterilisation is the most successful in terms of numbers of pregnancies achieved. With all tubal surgery there is an increased incidence of ectopic pregnancy.

Endometriosis can be treated with medication to stop periods in order to let the damaged tissues recover.

IVF (In Vitro Fertilisation) – the removal of a woman's ovum and fertilising it with the man's sperm in a 'test-tube', then replacing it in the woman's uterus) is also regarded as suitable by the medical profession for those with tubal obstructions. (Christians see ethical problems that leave a question mark over this methodology – see section below.)

iii) Sperm Problems

It is very difficult to work out from semen analysis alone what is wrong and whether it is curable. The only exception is where there is a zero or very low sperm count. Other low counts are very difficult to assess. The options for severe problems are:

- No sperm – either AID (Artificial Insemination by Donor) – using donor sperm and injecting it into the woman. Christians have real ethical problems with this! (see section below); or adoption; or, rarely, male tubal surgery if there is a blockage. In a few cases hormonal stimulating drugs.
- Very low sperm – the above plus IVF and IUI (Intrauterine Insemination) – the process of taking the man's semen and injecting it straight into the

uterus – bypassing the cervix. This has little ethical
difficulty as the sperm used belongs to the couple
concerned. There are also new techniques available
involving micro-injection of a sperm directly into
an ovum.

iv) Unexplained infertility

As mentioned above, this group has quite a high natural
pregnancy rate but the standard treatments offered are
GIFT (Gamete Intrafallopian Transfer) – the woman's ovum
is removed and mixed with sperm and the mixture injected
into the Fallopian tube before fertilisation takes place. This
is also the natural place for fertilisation to happen; it is
only how they got there that is unnatural. ZIFT (Zygote
IntraFallopian Transfer) – just like GIFT above, but the
sperm has already fertilised the ovum (Zygote simply
means a newly-fertilised egg) and IUI.

Other methods sometimes used by medics but all
ethically-suspect to a Christian include egg donation (using
another woman's ovum), sperm donation (AID above or this
in conjuction with IVF, IUI, GIFT or ZIFT). Egg and sperm
donation (getting pregnant with a baby where both ovum
and sperm are from a different couple), or embryo donation
(as above but with the egg and sperm already fertilised).

ETHICAL ISSUES

Everybody concerned with the treatment of infertility –
except a few extremists who think 'humans are only animals
anyway' – agree that there needs to be a line drawn somewhere in every area of medical ethics. Obviously different
people draw it in different places. Some would argue that
being able to do something that works is a good enough
argument to say that it is right. But that was the basis of
Hitler's experiments on children and others.

As Christians we know that God has given us an objective
way of assessing ethics, the Scriptures. However we also
know that people can read the same Bible and come to
different conclusions. Below we have outlined what we

consider to be the two main ethical issues Others may
disagree with us. But if, to be able to disagree, you have
to ignore anything of Scripture, we can assure you that the
actions you take will be out of line with God's revealed
order. One day you will have to live with the consequences
of your actions. Maybe the repercussions will be seen sooner
than we think!

There are two matters, in our understanding, that help
people determine the ethics of a medical technique or
treatment in the area of helping subfertile couples:

1) Whose ovum and sperm are being used? The couples'
   or someone else's?
      We fully understand the simplicity and therefore
   the apparent beauty of using someone else's sperm or
   ovum when yours are not working. But we still have
   to ask a question. What is the difference, in essence,
   between this and adultery? Yes, it is a very clinical
   version of it, but it is still rooted in the same place.

2) What happens to the human beings (the couple and the
   fertilsed eggs) involved?
      When we first heard of IVF (and similar in vitro
   methods of fertilisation, using the couples own ovum
   and sperm, e.g. ZIFT etc) it sounded like a simple way
   of helping the process along; a sort of match-making
   at a microscopic level. What the press doesn't shout
   about is the number of living human beings (embryos)
   who are 'manufactured' and then stored or destroyed;
   let alone the number of implanted people (embryos)
   who after implantation die and are miscarried. It is
   what the doctors call their 'success rate'. To give you
   an example, in a recent article[2] it was reported from
   research done that in 11 infertility clinics the average
   success rate was just under 18 per cent. That means
   that more than four out of five children are dying to
   feed this infatuation with having a baby 'of my own'.
   In case you are wondering, these are the same figures
   that the IVF enthusiasts are using to show us how well
   they are doing!

We do know that the basis of the above argument is the belief that a human being becomes a human being during the process of fertilisation – which we know is not just a moment in time. There has been much debate about this, particularly around the issue of abortion. We do not feel this is the place to rehearse this all over again; though we do however believe the correct biblical position (Ps 139; Jer 1:5) is that the life of a human being starts at the moment of conception.

More must be said about surrogate motherhood. Twice in Scripture this is used as a way for a woman to have children when infertile. First Sarah and then Rachel and Leah, the two wives of Jacob. At that point the Bible makes no overt moral judgment. It merely tells the story. The story in each case is one of extreme jealousy and rivalry, which certainly corresponds to some of the stories in the press over the last decade. Later in the Bible, Moses designates adultery as a sin punishable by death for both people involved. In the New Testament, both Jesus and Paul make it quite clear that God's best is that a man should be the husband of but one wife. All this evidence, and far more that could be outlined, tells us that surrogacy is so far outside the biblical ethical position that it is certainly ruled out for Christians, even if the whole world disagrees with us.

Hopefully both our silence on some subjects, and views on others, will have been helpful to you as you try to get a Christian perspective on these issues. If you are still struggling, there are many Christian ethicists who have done studies in these areas. May we suggest you write to CARE (53 Romney St, Westminster, London. SW1P 3RF) and they will be able to put you in touch with the relevant material or person.

SIX

PRAYING FOR HEALING

S ome would dispute whether healing is the correct word
to describe the process that changes an infertile couple
into one that has biological children. There is an argument
that neither of the couple are necessarily sick. However, for
the purposes of this book we shall stick to the idea that
the solving of infertility, as a condition, is called healing.
We certainly have a good biblical basis for this, as the
meaning of the words 'saving' and 'healing' in Scripture
are interchangeable.

Christians have been practising healing for almost 2000
years; ever since Jesus said, 'Heal the sick, raise the dead,
cleanse those who have leprosy, drive out demons. Freely
you have received, freely give' (Matt 10:8).

It has always been a controversial matter. In the early
days there are eye witness records of the release of God's
supernatural power in Jesus' name. It was one of the signs
of an apostle that through him healings took place. Later
the Roman Catholic Church introduced the idea of saints,
and the performing (always a strange word!) of miracles
and healings were essential for canonisation. Then, when
the western world began to develop modern medicine,
Christians began to see that healing was something that
God might achieve by his providence – the way he made
the world – as well as His power.

In the area of infertility it is particularly difficult to assess
if a miracle has happened. It is very unusual for any doctor
to say, 'It is impossible for you to have a child.' So, if a
couple does get pregnant after prayer, the doctors simply
say, 'There was always a probability that you would. A

low probability, but it is none the less possible that this happened by natural means.'

This does not worry us as Christians. Miracles are as much a matter of beating the probabilities, as being provable medically. It may be a coincidence that a particular couple became pregnant in the month immediately following prayer. But even a sceptic has to be amazed at how many coincidences of this kind seem to happen!

INFERTILITY 'HEALED' IN THE BIBLE

The Bible says many things about childlessness, and not always that it will be healed. But the central message is that, in certain circumstances, God does act in this area. Below is a list of those healed of infertility in the Bible – six in the Old Testament, and one in the New Testament.

Abraham & Sarah	Gen 15–21
Isaac & Rebekah	Gen 25:21–24
Jacob & Rachel	Gen 30:1 & 22–24
Samson's Parents	Judg 13
Samuel's Parents	1 Sam 1
Shunammite Woman	2 Kings 4:14–17
John the Baptist's Parents	Luke 1:7–25

Some may say that this is only seven incidents in the whole of the Scriptures. May we say that not only are seven incidents a very large number for any subject in the Bible, but these are also some of the most significant passages for understanding both old and new covenants. This shows that the normal thing for a believer to do when she/he faces involuntary childlessness is to PRAY! There may be many reasons why this may not 'work'. But this is what the Bible suggests that we should do.

INFERTILITY 'HEALED' IN THE MODERN WORLD

We have spoken to quite a few people who claim this experience. They have been diagnosed as subfertile by a doctor. As Christians they have asked their church – or a visiting speaker – to pray for them. They have then become pregnant within the next two or three months.

We have two difficulties at this point. Most of these folks cannot prove a miracle has taken place (as we have explained above). They therefore do not want their story published! This is very much in line with what Jesus said to a number of those he healed in the Bible (Luke 5:14).

So we have decided to give you just five examples of the kind of thing that seems to happen very regularly. However, if those who read this book would like to send us stories of medically verifiable miracles of infertility healed, we would love to put a few into the next edition!?

Case 1: Sovereign God or what? – as told by Ellie Mumford
A girl, known particularly to my husband; she had been very very ill for a long time with a horrendous form of colitis (inflammation of the colon). She was married. She had been dreadfully abused as a child. And she was infertile. Just everything was grotty! She's . . . a lovely just lovely young woman. Well last September the Lord graciously healed her, and her colitis was completely taken away. Then about three or four weeks ago, the Lord (following prayer) fell on her to such a degree that, when she got back to her feet, she said it was as if she had no past; no memory; no abuse. And she is now newly pregnant! Now is that sovereign God or what? Isn't that a wonderful thing?[1]

Case 2: The RE Head
A couple of years ago we were involved in taking some RE lessons in a secondary school. The RE head was a friendly lady in her early forties. She told us that she had been a career teacher ever since she was diagnosed as being permanently infertile. Without being too worried about it, she and her husband had just got on with life.

However, her mother was distraught. The RE teacher had no particular Christian faith, but her mother was a Pentecostal believer. She kept saying that the Lord had promised that her daughter would conceive.

At the end of one month, well over ten years after having given up on having children, this lady was surprised because her period did not happen. She popped in to her doctor for a pregnancy test. Definitely positive.

'To be honest by that stage it was quite inconvenient. But, of course, we were overjoyed,' she told us, 'But mother went wild! "Didn't I tell you the Lord had promised you a child? The Lord always answers prayer!". Personally,' she said, 'I wasn't sure if it was the Lord or a burst of hormones. But I don't suppose that matters so much really.'

Case 3: One does, one doesn't

Two Christian couples were both diagnosed as being infertile. They both went for prayer. In one case there was no apparent reason. In the other it was such a clear case of endometriosis that the doctors suggested it was very likely to make them permanently childless. Neither was healed. Being in the same boat they decided to live in the same house.

A little while later, the couple in which the woman had endometriosis went forward for prayer at a Christian meeting. There was a particular atmosphere of faith – even certainty – as those praying did business in the spiritual world. They went home and shortly after conceived.

What was disturbing about this is that the other couple are still childless. You may have thought they could go on living in the same house and all four enjoy the new arrival. Sadly the fact that their friends now had a child was so disturbing for the other couple that they decided that was not possible.

Even prayer being answered can cause some problems.

Case 4: Visitation

One Christian church regularly visits all the people that live in their area. One day they knocked on a front door and a young couple answered. 'We're Christians. We wondered if you have any needs that we could pray for/about?'

The couple were overjoyed. 'Yes please. We're infertile. Could you please pray that we have a child?'

Of course the Christians were more than happy to pray for that. Right there and then they joined hands and called on God, binding and loosing things in the heavens.

A little while later someone else from the church visited the young couple to 'follow up' the previous incident. Instantly they were invited in and a baby was thrust into their arms. 'This is the miracle that God did. Your people prayed that we would have a child. And we have!'

Wow! thought the Christians! and tried to get involved in all the excitement . . . and also to find out some of the details. As they asked questions they soon discovered that the couple had just been given this baby for *adoption*. Sometimes people with no Christian faith find it easier to see a miracle than those of us who, although we know Jesus theoretically, like to have everything scientifically proven.

Case 5: A gift indeed! – Chris and Mary's story
It has become a family joke that our son David was conceived while his parents were in separate beds five miles apart! It's a story of the faithfulness of God, despite setbacks, and how He can use medical care and prayer to His glory.

When we married, we had slight suspicions that having children might be difficult. Chris had undescended testes which were only lowered by an operation when he was 12 (nowadays considered *far* too late!).

Nevertheless we waited until Mary had qualified as a nurse before planning a family and then asked our GP if there was a problem. After tests he declared that there was no reason why children shouldn't come naturally; but we checked the figures and discovered he was wrong.

The number and condition of the sperm were much lower than normal. In fact, outside the range where natural conception would be expected.

We began to pray and committed the situation to the Lord. Even before marriage, Chris had a promise from God that he would have children and now that

was re-affirmed through prayer and Bible reading. We
began to expect a pregnancy and specifically asked
that at some stage we'd have a boy (to be called
David – we've always liked the name which means
'beloved').

Both of us yearned for children and Mary gave up
nursing after qualifying, with the ambition of helping
alongside Chris in parish work and being a wife and
mother.

But nothing happened.

Each month went by with no change and the arrival
of every period (at least in the early days) was devastating. Mary, especially, was angry, depressed and
confused. Why could everyone else have babies but
not us? Were we being punished? Did God consider
us unfit parents? All the questions came – and the sadness. She felt unfulfilled and ashamed that a Christian
should be this way.

Chris tried to cope, but kept repeating the same
things: 'God promised us children, we *must* trust
Him for the timing.' Really there were no answers,
we could only console each other and pray when we
could manage it.

At that time there were few published resources to
help but our family and the congregation of our new
church were a tremendous support. Chris' brother
(who has the same problem) became father to Matthew
and, later, to Frances. This was really encouraging. But
still nothing happened for us.

However, all who were praying agreed that the Lord
had made a promise. Each time we hit rock-bottom the
Bible reading on the next day turned out to be about
a childless couple conceiving, or Christ found another
way of strengthening our faith. We often doubted but
somehow still hoped and believed at the same time.

Gradually we handled it better, though an early
miscarriage set us back a bit. Abraham and Sarah,
from the book of Genesis, became very important to
us. We didn't feel as full of faith as they seemed,

but even they had times of doubt, when God had to encourage them.

The miscarriage brought grief, but it also meant that pregnancy could happen. We began to pray about seeking medical help to conceive.

The doors seemed open wide. A local doctor passed us to an expert at the 'Chelsea Hospital for Women'. They treated us with tremendous patience and kindness and soon we were both having tests.

We were asked about the 'test tube baby' programme and told that the waiting list on the NHS was 3 years. So we began to think through all the moral problems involved.

We don't believe that the use of medical techniques is wrong in itself but draw the line firmly at the creation of embryos (fertilised eggs) which are discarded or kept by freezing. In other words, we think that you can do what you like with sperm and eggs when they are apart but when brought together any resulting embryo (even if considered 'faulty') should have an immediate chance to live because he or she is human.

We were told about a method called GIFT (Gamete Intro-Fallopian Transfer) where a couple's own eggs and sperm are treated and then mixed as they are put back into the wife. This seemed ideal for us, although we were warned that it has a low success rate.

The hospital checked us for the treatment and then tried to persuade Mary not to have it. 'You have less than 5% chance of conceiving in this way. If you do, it will be a miracle.'

We went ahead, confident that the Lord was in it all.

The pills and injections for Mary multiplied up to the 'big week' so she would produce several eggs. Scans only showed one but other tests suggested more, so they reluctantly continued the programme. (We actually had 4 perfect ones, so *could* have ended up with quads!)

Suddenly everything outside the treatment seemed to be under pressure. In the same fortnight Mary had a driving test, we had an interview for our present parish, and church work seemed to treble. But we only suspected spiritual attack when the rest happened.

On the day before the important part of the programme, Chris tore a muscle in his back and retired to bed. The next morning he had a raging temperature, felt awful and kept fainting. A friend took us to the hospital where Mary was to have the small operation for GIFT and Chris supposedly produce a sperm sample.

Feeling half-dead he went to the loo for this purpose. Time ticked away while he fainted again. The sample had to be in by 9 am! We made it with a couple of minutes to spare and then Chris was whisked back to the other bed 5 miles away!

Everything else went well and then began the waiting and half-hoping time until they could see if Mary was pregnant. Other couples in our batch had been given better odds, but sadly were all disappointed; yet our tests were positive and in 6 weeks we saw David as a tiny heartbeat on the scanner. The Lord had triumphed!

The pregnancy went reasonably well (though Chris stole the limelight early on with the discovery and successful treatment of testicular cancer).

And now we have this gorgeous baby; the perfect fulfilment of the Lord's promise. We expect Him to provide brothers and sisters too, perhaps through the NHS again, but at the moment we are just thrilled with David. He really is God's GIFT to us![2]

There is a postscript to this story. The doctors soon discovered that Chris' testicular cancer had now completely destroyed his ability to produce sperm. So Chris and Mary resigned themselves to the certainty that David would be their only child, even though they continued to ask the Lord.

And then it happened. Mary became pregnant again. In Chris' words, 'People can argue about possibilities and probabilities as long as they like when we talk about how David was born, but this time saying it is a miracle is the only option!'

So . . . there are a few examples. Ask at your local Bible-believing Christian church and we can almost guarantee they will tell you some more.

THE PROBLEMS

The best way to illustrate this is by letting Sally Haworth tell her story. She and husband Bryn – who is a well-known Christian musician – know both the problems of being prayed for and the glories of hearing a personal liberating word from Jesus.

We knew when we got married that it was unlikely that we would have children and I had been advised that surgical treatment, although possible, had little chance of success. We weren't Christians at that time and were living a rock and roll lifestyle; travelling a good deal, moving from one rented home to another. Most of our musician friends who were married were having affairs as they travelled from town to town, while their wives were at home with the children. We had no home of our own, no furniture, no fixed income, and we really thought very little, if at all, about the need to have children.

From the first day we met we were friends, and that has always been a great strength in our relationship. If I thought about children in those days, it was only to think that this world was a terrible place into which to bring them.

After 18 months of marriage we became Christians, and our lifestyle didn't change much in an outward sense, as we built up our personal relationship with Jesus and enjoyed the teaching of a good evangelical church. Most of our friends were still musicians with varied lifestyles. Some had children, some were married, or living together, or single. The subject of children was not very relevant, and our childlessness caused none of our friends concern; although our new love for Jesus certainly disturbed a few!

In those early years one incident has stuck in my mind. A woman from the church we went to, who was a very spiritual and charismatic lady, and who worked as a nurse in an infants ward, came to us with a dream she'd had. She dreamt that we had a baby, born in the house we were then living in, and it was born dead. The dream gave me the creeps for a long time, but the thing that struck me most was her intense concern that we should have children, despite her rather discouraging dream. It was an attitude I was to become increasingly aware of.

As we grew in the things of God and experienced more freedom in His Spirit, we were particularly attracted to a fellowship which was doing a wonderful job getting people saved and experiencing God's power in healing, and in many other ways. We went to see the leader of the movement to find out a bit more, with a view to joining. Everything was going wonderfully until he addressed me, very straightforwardly, saying, '. . . of course if you want to be in God's will you will have to get children.'

By that time I had already been prayed for on various occasions to be able to have children. I was very open for it to happen. In fact, if I had become pregnant I would have loved it. What a nice thing to have my husband's child! But I wasn't going to destroy my marriage through getting desperate about it. I had thought about adopting, but knew we were bad candidates; by that time I was 35; we had no home of our own; no regular income! There wasn't a lot going for us. So I really didn't know how we were going to 'get' children. The incident left me feeling guilty and disobedient about something I couldn't change.

I've been in meetings when every childless woman is invited to stand for healing prayer. I used to have faith for it, but as that diminished I found myself standing anyway because people knew I was childless and to be seen not to stand was to be seen as disobedient. At one more recent meeting the church leader said, 'There is someone else here, someone I know, who is childless, and if you don't stand now you will be in disobedience to God.' He was a church leader I loved and respected, and I knew he was addressing me. I felt intense pressure to stand. But I couldn't. I no longer believed it would happen, or that it was God's will for me. It was a depressing incident.

Shortly after this we were at a conference and an American pastor, who was part of the worship band came to me one day. He said he had sought God the night before about me and the subject of children, and he had felt God say clearly, 'Sally will not bear children, but she will be the mother of many.' I felt such enormous relief and freedom, and the love of God touched me.

It is true that we have been spiritual parents to many people. We have seen them born into the kingdom and grow into maturity in Christ, and it has been a source of enormous pleasure to us. We have also delighted greatly in other people's children. Not having any of our own, we don't automatically adopt an adult/child position with them, so they are free to treat us as friends.

We spent several years in one wonderful church movement which increasingly focused its vision on young couples with children. It was quite a fight to stay in there and feel wanted, and I know that many of the older and also the single people felt the same way. It's so wonderful to find Jesus in this sad old world; but so tragic if you find that the church does not really seem to want you as you are. We live in a

world which is torn and bruised because it has fallen a
long way from God's best. The couple with 2.2 children
is no longer, and never was, the world's norm; in fact
they are the minority. God it seems has allowed many
of us to remain outside society's 'nice and acceptable'
boundaries in order that the world may find a people
it can relate to within His kingdom.

As time goes by we both have pangs about being
childless. We wonder what our children would have
been like, and we would both have enjoyed them.
We have great sympathy for those who desperately
want children but can't for one reason or another. But
for ourselves we feel very fortunate that it has never
been a source of distress. God has given us so much
together and in His kingdom that our lives have not
been poorer for lack of children.

We are so grateful to Sally and Bryn for allowing us to
share this with you. Somehow they have captured both the
frustration with the well-meaning but meddling attitude
that is so prevalent in the charismatic church today, and
the very healthy attitude of, 'Don't let it get you down!'
What's more, when you meet them you know it's all true.
They are at peace with God and enjoying life.

Some reading this may find it difficult. You have been
brought up with praying for and proclaiming every possible
kind of healing – in the hope that you might get a few!
We understand how you feel. So let's explore this subject
further.

Being infertile is a highly emotional and disturbing experience. Being prayed for is also very personal. If the process
of putting the two together is not handled very sensitively
it can be very painful.

The problem starts with those who are praying for the
childless couple. So often, in Christian churches in 1990s
UK, these dear disciples treat the opportunity as a challenge
to their spirituality and faith. They therefore seem to delight
in the fact that they have a chance to 'get the breakthrough'.

They may want to show off to their friends that they have said 'the right words' and 'got a result'. They will therefore often be loud, aggressive, boastful and treat the couple as an object rather than hurting people.

This is clearly not the model of ministry suggested by Scripture, or modelled by Jesus or the apostles.

A little knowledge is still a dangerous thing!

Please do not think we are simply criticising. The truth is, we are confessing that we have been there and done it. On one occasion (over ten years ago!) I made a terrible mistake. At a meeting with worship and preaching, there was an opportunity for anyone who would like prayer to come to the front. Among others, a young couple knelt at the rail. It just happened that I – still very inexperienced – was asked to pray that their infertility would be healed. There followed an intense time of calling on the Lord. Somewhere in the midst I felt the words, 'In a year's time they will have a baby'. Without hesitation I spoke this out.

At the time I assumed that the couple was reasonably stable and would take my words in the experimental attitude in which they were given. They looked like mature Christians who would know 1 Thessalonians 5:19–21 'Do not treat prophecies with contempt. Test everything. Hold on to the good!'. But in this couple's state of extreme wishful thinking their measured rationality had gone out the window. As soon as the meeting was over they contacted the infertility clinic and cancelled their treatment and took their name off the adoption list. A year later we were in the area and had the embarrassment of meeting them. There was no baby! There is still no baby! It was a ghastly mistake . . . born out of arrogance, inexperience and self-centredness. They were very forgiving. We learnt a very important lesson!

Please learn by our mistakes. Do not make your own!

A friend of ours recently had a similar problem. She is also childless. The cause of this is that she is single. She is a Christian and would like to find a husband but has not met the right man. Some friends were praying with her when one of them said that they 'had a picture' (in his imagination) of her with children on her lap. He said that he 'felt God was saying' that she would soon have a child . . . and by inference, find a man to marry.

Excitement would have been an understatement! She bounded in to see us brimming over with this 'prophecy'.

A year later not much had happened. Disillusionment set in. She went to see a couple of people who she and we respect very highly – Roger and Faith Forster. She asked them to pray with her that the depression she was experiencing would lift.

When they heard the cause they said something like,

> We really believe that God wants to heal people and provide for people in the area of marriage and children, and continue to pray with all our heart with anyone who asks. But, except in extraordinary circumstances, we now consider it unwise pastorally to prophesy to people in the two areas of marriage partner and/or future children.

We agree! It must be noted that following prayer our friend's depression completely lifted. And now, much to our surprise, an amazing gift in ministering to crèche-age children has begun to be evident. She now leads an Adults and Toddlers Group and is responsible for all our Under 5s. And she is still single.

Therefore the 'picture' of the children on her knee, looks as if it was the word of God. The interpretation – about getting married and having children – seems to have been simply imagination. The Bible explains how you can tell the difference. 'If what a prophet proclaims in the name of the LORD does not take place or come true, that is a message the LORD has not spoken. That prophet has spoken presumptuously. Do not be afraid of him' (Deut 18:22).

So how should we receive prayer? In hope and faith in God's goodness towards us; with the understanding that there is a spiritual struggle going on; and with our minds and free wills switched on!

It is your own responsibility to believe or not believe whether what you are hearing is from God or not. You cannot shift the responsibility to the person praying for you. You cannot blame them for your own mistakes.

UNCHRISTIAN VERSIONS OF SUPERNATURAL HEALING

One of the most dangerous states you can ever be in is to be in need of supernatural intervention and not be worried where you get it from. Wanting healing from terminal disease, wanting a job, wanting to get married or have a child. In these circumstances people regularly reach out for a spiritual solution.

It is very similar to when someone is in deep financial trouble. You can go to your family, a reputable bank or a loan shark. Probably the easiest to get the money from is the loan shark! But you may be paying for the privilege for the rest of your life!

There are two sources of spiritual power. There is your heavenly Father. In Jesus Christ he has already paid off your debts. With him it is not just supernatural power on demand. It has to be for your best, and for the best of his good purposes.

But there are others who will provide you with miracles: New Agers, Occultists, Astrologists, Tealeaf Readers, Pseudo-Christian Cults (e.g., 'Christian' Spiritualism, Swedenborgism, Jehovah's Witnesses, Mormons, Ba'hai, etc), Hinduism, Islam, Buddhism, etc. But anything that does not accept the Triune God – Father, Son and Holy Spirit, is a spiritual loan shark.

This is how the Bible puts it:

> If a prophet, or one who foretells by dreams, appears among you and announces to you a miraculous sign or wonder, and if the sign or wonder of which he has spoken takes place, and he says, 'Let us follow other gods' (gods you have not known) 'and let us worship them,' you must not listen to the words of that prophet or dreamer. The LORD your God is testing you to find out whether you love him with all your heart and

with all your soul. It is the LORD your God you must follow, and him you must revere. Keep his commands and obey him; serve him and hold fast to him. That prophet or dreamer must be put to death, because he preached rebellion against the LORD your God . . .

It goes on . . .

If your very own brother, or your son or daughter, or the wife you love, or your closest friend secretly entices you, saying, 'Let us go and worship other gods' (gods that neither you nor your fathers have known, gods of the peoples around you, whether near or far, from one end of the land to the other), do not yield to him or listen to him. Show him no pity. Do not spare him or shield him. You must certainly put him to death. Your hand must be the first in putting him to death, and then the hands of all the people . . .

(Deut 13:1–9)

Gladly these days we do not need to put people to death. Since Jesus came and died for even this scale of sin, repentance and forgiveness are possible. In Christ we must love the one speaking while still maintaining the attitude of complete hostility to the lies and deception that come from their mouths.

Please do not be fooled. Those who suggest getting healing from these false teachings may be both persuasive and completely sincere; believing totally that they are doing you a favour. Treat the person as your friend but the teaching as your enemy!

So . . . to sum up:
Yes!   There is a God who heals in Jesus' Name.
Yes!   The Bible does teach God specifically heals infertility.
Yes!   If it is for your good and the good of the furtherance of his purposes, then God will heal you.

Yes!   There may be a struggle in prayer before you get
the breakthrough.
Yes!   God loves you and is on your side, even if you
never have a child.
   But No! Don't be fooled into thinking its worth leaving
God behind, just to have a baby!

SEVEN

GENDER MATTERS

At the beginning of creation God made them male and female.
(Mark 10:6)

The struggles and strengths of women and men facing infertility can be very different. Some of this is caused by the expectations society places on the different genders. But the physiology, psychology and spiritual nature of male and female are very different. In this chapter we want to examine first the female, then the male, challenges and opportunities.

FEMALE

From a very early age a child is aware of his or her gender. It affects their relationship with everybody and everything. Different forms of significance are looked for and found from their parents and from the wider world. Society finds stereotypes for these responses. Of course some people do not fit into these, and we must make allowances for them, but the exceptions still reveal the general rule.

In this chapter our aim is to list a few of these pressures as they affect women, and discuss how they relate to their possible responses to being infertile. We think you will find this list useful as you examine your reactions and seek to understand yourself.

Puberty

It is regularly said that girls grow up earlier than boys. These days female puberty in the western world is getting earlier and earlier. For a young girl the process of having her first period is very dramatic, personal and daunting. It brings home to her very powerfully that she is apparently made to have a sexual and reproductive function, and it is not a one-off experience. Every month there is a reminder. Every month their hormones go round their cycle.

These hormones do not only make the physical changes of the menstrual cycle. They also affect the woman's feelings and hungers. By feelings we mean happiness, sadness, being uptight, relaxed, tearful or energetic. By hungers we refer to her desire for exercise, food, company, sex, significance, tidiness, a 'nest', etc.

In the 1960s puberty affected the average girl at 15–16. This was earlier than before and, with the introduction of the pill, led to a wild time. Now some girls are reaching puberty at 11–12. By 13–14 they can be already completely confused. By 15–16 many are already mothers. They have tried to find significance the way society and the rush of their hormones has suggested. And now they are trying to be strong enough to cope with it all.

Others will have abortions, be on the pill or taking some other kind of contraception. Their experiences of sex may be multiple, extreme and dangerous (including VD, AIDS, etc). Each of these things can seriously damage the emotions, spirit or physical child-bearing ability of a woman. The effect may not show immediately. But later, if she finally finds a stable relationship/marriage and suffers from infertility, the roots of the problem may well be found back in those early years after her first period.

Oh how wonderful it is to know Jesus! Without him some of these problems attached to young women, through little fault of their own, would be completely insoluble. But through the power of Jesus' resurrection it is possible to have the past forgiven, healed and unlocked. You do not need to be held by the problems of the past.

Maternal vs Paternal Instinct

All psychological observations are by nature generalisations. There are those who do not fit the regular pattern. This does not mean that they are odd, or 'not normal'. It is just an expression of the unique identity of each of the human race.

Having said that, it seems clear to us that women and men react very differently! There may be some truth in the idea that this is socially conditioned but not so much as the trendy academics would like to make out.

From very early in life most little girls want dolls. One of the best sellers at present is a doll that looks just like a real baby. Little girls will nurse, cuddle, change, dress and take baby for walks. There is a strong instinctive fascination.

Our niece and nephew recently had a little sister born into their family. It was amazing to watch the contrast between the two older children in response to the baby. The little girl followed Mummy about watching every move. Anytime she could be involved in holding, changing, feeding, her enthusiasm was extraordinary.

The little boy was very different. He went to the hospital once. The next time the family was going to visit the new arrival it was, 'Do I have to go? I've seen it once!' And when they came home he would check she was OK every now and then but otherwise get on with his life.

However, as the baby grew up her brother's attitude developed. He is now besotted with her. Not in the sense of wanting to change her nappies, but in an insatiable desire to protect, care and indulge her. All those caricatures of fathers are being seen in a developing form in a little man.

A friend of ours observed that many women can get broody just looking at a baby. Men play along, but hormonal influences do not affect them in the same way. They are stimulated visually, but it is normally more by the potential mother than by the angelic offspring of some other family.

However, when a man sees a child that he has fathered,

things are very different. By this time the mother has normally moved into 'practical' mode. She is focused on caring on a day-by-day basis. But new dads are well known for being very emotional and starting to speak in poetic terms. 'I did that!', 'To think that is my son!', 'This little girl is my princess!'

This contrast in response can mean that the woman of an infertile couple will be the first to feel the extremes of anxiety. Her husband can appear to be unaffected. He has not yet really come to think that a baby will fit into their household. He knows it is natural. He likes the idea. He knows he will be upset if there really is a problem. 'But we'll cross that bridge when we come to it.' He is determined that it will not disturb him too much either way. He sets out to 'be strong' for the woman he loves.

She, on the other hand, does not just want him to be strong. She expects and wants him to be involved, to be as upset as she is. She rushes to doctors, arranges appointments, and always seems to have to drag a commitment out of her man.

Some of you reading this will be upset by our generalisations, but our purpose here is to tell you that this is normal healthy behaviour. You may not like it but most men behave this way! The extreme case is normally when the man is confronted with the request for a sperm test. Suddenly he is disturbed, afraid, anxious; sometimes even agressive.

Why, you might ask, are we putting all this stuff about the male response in the section on women's psychology? The answer is simple. Some women get more upset about the contrast between their own feelings and the apparent attitude of their man, than they do about the infertility itself. It can make a woman feel that, 'He doesn't really care!' But it is not true. *If you remain childless for the long term or forever, all studies suggest that it is the man who finds it most difficult to cope with.* Particularly if the biological problem relates to the sperm. But, whatever the reason, he will probably feel it is something he should be able to solve. Failure is a much more frightening word for a man than for his wife.

Cultural Visibility and Expectation

A woman without children is more obvious than a man without children. Why? Because, despite a few adventurous house-husbands, it is still normal for women to change their lifestyles to look after children, whereas men normally stay on the same life/career direction. Even if both have external employment, it is likely that the woman's job will be the one most affected by having to arrange child care or be back in time for the kids to get home from school.

A married woman between 25 and 40 without children continually raises the question, 'When will she have a baby?' And what goes through people's minds, regularly comes out of their mouths!

'You'll be next!' is always a side comment beside the cot of the family newborn. 'So when do you think you and Hugo will be starting a family?' is a question which regularly gets thrust in my face moments before preaching to an expectant congregation. 'Who do you get to look after yours?' is said more often than you would think possible!

It is not sympathy which is being looked for. Just acceptance that not having children is just as *normal* as having a complete brood. But, however hard we campaign for it, human nature will remain the same. It is natural to be curious about these issues. Today's politically correct culture will not suddenly wipe out hormones, expectations or what is considered normal behaviour.

So don't fight against it. Get ready for it.

If you are a woman, at a childbearing age, who does not have children, people look, ask questions, make comments, make faces, whisper, thrust babies in your face and generally do things that are going to disturb you. Whatever you do, don't hold it against them. If it hurts, tell them! It does no harm to educate. But recognise that they are more confused by your situation than you are. After all, you have had time to think and feel it through. To them, it is all new.

'Wife and Mother' Feelings of Duty to Husband

Many women say that their own expectations are far harder to deal with than those imposed on them by others.

Somehow the very fact that they are making love to a man makes them want to be 'a good wife and mother'. In their mind the two go together. They say things like, 'How can I be a proper wife to him if I can't give him any children?' Even at the beginning of a sexual relationship there is the implicit – sometimes explicit – cry from the woman, 'I want to have your baby!'

The problem here is that infertility can get the woman questioning the validity of the marriage. No longer is it she and her husband against a world that does not understand. Now she feels she is not fulfilling her side of the marriage contract. Questions begin to arise in her mind as to whether – even though they desperately love and need one another – they should really separate.

Illogical? Of course it is! But don't be surprised if you feel this way. Most infertile women do. Even apparently logical women. It is natural. But it is also dangerous. You must get control of it!

What makes a marriage is loving one another, mutual friendship and care, living together and satisfying each other sexually. To have and to hold, in sickness and in health, for richer for poorer, 'til death us do part! All apparently infertility does is give you a chance to practise some of the above! If you have a child, that is a *bonus!*

Obsession

Whether it is hormonal, cultural, genetic, mental or just a character trait we don't know! But some infertile women become completely obsessed with having a child. The passion can rage for months or years. It can sweep through your life like a forest fire consuming everything else in its path.

This is the most destructive symptom of infertility. It is not universal but it is the caricature. If you fail in this area then all those you love and all other options that might be important either with or without children can be so damaged that, even if you get pregnant, repair is almost impossible.

Some of the signs of obsession include:

- studying your temperature charts at regular intervals during the day
- commanding your husband into bed to 'get it done' even when there is no basis for this being the best time
- failing to turn up for appointments
- finding yourself staring at babies when out shopping
- having days off 'sick' from work even when the doctor has not suggested this
- letting other important dreams slip
- refusing to see your parents or siblings
- letting your spouse down on something you know is important to them
- seeking treatment from weird sources
- or a multitude of other strange behaviours.

If you are experiencing difficulties getting pregnant and you are beginning to seek treatment, watch over each other. Regularly sit down and talk about your feelings. Ask yourselves whether you are destroying any relationships, opportunities or dreams in your present pursuit of a child. Honestly discuss whether you think it is worth it. Come to conclusions on which you both can agree.

However, if you or your partner are getting concerned that you are becoming obsessed, do not keep the worry between yourselves. Talk to your GP or contact a counsellor. They may be able to let you get a perspective on the issues you are facing. This process may even help you get to the root of the problems and therefore be able to cope better with the next phase of treatment.

Menopausal Crisis

For women the biological clock does tick away. For most, sometime in their late 40s, they stop producing eggs and having periods. For some, this is much earlier – but premature menopause can now sometimes be treated.

For the two or three years before this, something in the woman begins to tell them to get on with it, if they are going to. According to Professon Winston there is no evidence that the woman's level of fertility will go up or down over this time, only the sense of urgency.

This pressure is quite logical. The menopause does mark the end of a woman's childbearing opportunity (assuming you rule out the methods being used in Italy to rejuvenate women's wombs through chemicals and then implant donor embryos).

For most women this is good news. Even for infertile/childless women. At least from then on the sense of choice or pressure to have one more try is completely over. They can at last get on with their life knowing that this is the way it is. The water is under the bridge!

But how does the menopause work?

It is thought to be caused by the fluctuations – and final decline – of various hormones in a woman's body. These not only produce the physical changes experienced each month, but also the desire for sex or child bearing.

Just because a woman is infertile does not mean she will not go through a menopausal experience. Many childless women continue to have periods and hormones quite normally. Others who had great hormone deficiencies through most of their life can suddenly get a real burst just before the menopause.

So, even if you seem to have fully 'come to terms' with being childless, and life has settled into a happy rhythm, it may not be over. Quite unexpectedly feelings you thought you had left far behind, return. Thoughts you had rationalised away, can come flooding back with a vengeance. Tearfulness, anger, resentment all rebound onto the surface of your mind. It does not happen for every woman, but for some it can be extreme.

If this is happening to you – or someone near you – may we suggest at least talking to the relevant GP. Hormone replacement – or balancing – therapy is working better and better. Our feelings are affected by chemicals in our body. Not exclusively – we still make choices! But we can at least settle our feelings by settling the balance of the chemicals – particularly when it is unnaturally fluctuating.

Post Menopausal Infertility Treatment

Recently a doctor in Italy has started giving hormone and other infertility treatment to women who are post menopausal. The result of this has been babies born to women who would previously have been regarded as beyond the age of pregnancy. There has obviously been much debate about the ethics of this treatment.

We found ourselves discussing this with a couple who are friends of ours, and also infertile – Doug and Anne Holt. Doug is a vicar in Ealing while Anne has worked in education and been active in the CARE movement.

Anne shared with us that one of the things that has made her most angry in the last few years has been the introduction of the treatment of post-menopausal women. She said she had been looking forward to passing 50 because then people would have to stop asking her if she was going to have children.

It used to be the wonderful age when you could know it was impossible and therefore let go of even the faint dreams that were left. It used to be like a watershed time that I longed to have passed. No longer would there be any reason for feeling guilty that you were not seeking treatment. No longer would there be a need to explain. But now, they have even taken that away!

There are many reasons to disapprove of the Italian treatment. But Anne's comments reveal a very important issue. Even in this world's fallen state, God has put into its design the opportunity of rest. In any activity under heaven there is a need for a time when the pressure is off. We must not let the world steal this from us, especially in the case of those who have already suffered so much from being infertile in the first place.

Even if you have invested days, weeks or years into trying to get pregnant; if you have failed and you have passed through the menopause – stop fretting. Take some rest from your efforts. Find some joy in the rest of your days from some other area of life.

MALE

I never thought I had difficulties sharing my feelings until I met Sharon. We were driving from A to B and paused at some traffic lights. Out of the blue I heard Sharon say, 'Which method of contraception do you want to use?' I was speechless, and the truth is I still find it hard talking about such intimate matters. Maybe it is true that women find it easier.

There is a natural assumption in most couples that any difficulties in fertility will probably relate to female biological problems. The facts say otherwise. The ratio of medically diagnosed infertility problems from male to female is 1:1. That means in about half the cases the medical problems relate to the sperm.

Put simply, low fertility is found in about 1 in 10 of men. It is therefore relatively common, and not something to be self-conscious about.

Easier said than done!

In our experience those who truly 'go to pieces' because they are childless are much more likely to be men than women. This is not always the case, but it is so often difficult to see how upset a man is until it bursts forth like a volcano. Women get equally upset, but they are so much better at letting it out bit by bit.

In this chapter we want to explore some of the particularly male difficulties with infertility. Our aim is to raise issues for you. This way the pressure can be confronted bit by bit. The need for total collapse might then be averted.

The New Man

It is commonly agreed that we live in a time of male identity crisis. Traditional roles are disappearing. Macho jobs are being replaced by machinery, and jobs that do not require physical strength can equally easily be done by women. Therefore the need for the man to be the bread winner has declined.

So what should a man do? In most situations the husband is still expected to have a job. He also is expected to do the washing up, a bit of cooking, hoovering and general administration around the house. Most still expect the man to do the DIY, although many women are far better at decorating. Then there is the traditional garden shed or allotment. Maybe a bit of sport. But most of all the man's role is to give Mum a break with the kids and regain his childhood while giving them a 'fun day out with Daddy'.

However unclear this may appear to be, all you need to do is watch the movies and you will see it expressed again and again. What really matters in life is 'your family'. When all the deals, money, fun, sin and power plays are over . . . 'who do you go home to?'.

So few men believe in anything beyond this. Nationalism and war are outdated. Sport is beginning to be seen as almost as hypocritical as politics. An understanding of real Christianity – including God's purpose for each life – has been drained by media interference, church incompetence and emptiness. Even the unions have been tainted by yuppy slick image making. It is instinctive for a man to want to achieve something important. Children can appear to be the only possible visible expression of that desire being fulfilled.

So what happens to a man who cannot have children?

Not much immediately. But slowly, slowly, unless he begins to see hope dawn in another direction, the darkness and despair of an apparently meaningless life begin to envelope him.

Actually a similar thing is happening to a great number of men who have children. But somehow infertility acts as a magnet drawing all the other feelings of insecurity, emptiness and depression. They were already there under the surface. Childlessness just allows them to escape the close guard; it gives a man a reason to believe that he should let them rule – and maybe even destroy – his life. And there is nothing more uninspiring and tedious than a man indulging in self-pity.

POSTERITY

If a man from an infertile couple is to leave something for posterity he must break this self-destructive cycle.

Most men know this. That's why they try to avoid the sperm test in the first place. They believe that if they don't know, it cannot hold them. Although this is against the present media-sponsored ideas, it may be wiser than we think! The only reason we can gain from knowing is if we can do something about the problem we find. And, if the doctors are honest, there is not a lot they can do about low sperm counts. So, no sperm test – no low sperm count – no reason to feel depressed. Lots of reason to make love to your wife. Which is enough to keep most men happy!

Happiness is a very important key to achieving anything. Self-pity destroys your energy to achieve other things in life. A strong sense of well-being leaves a man striving for the next mountain peak. Before you know it, he could be investing his life in something he can be really proud of. Childlessness may come up every now and then, but you will hear him say, 'We're disappointed, but there are so many other things in our life that we are fulfilled.' Some may say that they would not believe him. But from personal experience I can tell you that the critic would be wrong!

Our friends, Bryn and Sally Haworth, who we quoted in chapter 6, cannot have children. But they are happy. Bryn has always been a brilliant guitar player and singer/song writer. Sally has travelled, managed, organised and sound engineered. They have been a team. There was a time of investigations into the reasons that no child had come along. But they were living with a dream and a calling, and they knew that they were good at what they did. They knew they were affecting people's lives and the fruit of their efforts would be seen in the next generation.

When we asked them, 'How has infertility damaged your life?'

They looked at one another and the essence of their reply was this. 'I know people won't necessarily believe this. This is our life and we are wonderfully happy with it. When we think of how different it might have been if we had children it is almost frightening. Most of the things we have done together we couldn't have done. Most of the things we have achieved we probably wouldn't have gone for. Far from damaging our life, infertility is one of the factors that has made our life what it is.'

The Change Over

The most dangerous time emotionally for most infertile couples is receiving the results of the sperm test. As we have said, up until this moment the common assumption is that the difficulty is with the woman's reproductive system. Because the man's equipment is so much smaller, we assume it has less parts that can go wrong.

If it is discovered that there is no apparent reason why the woman cannot conceive, but the man's sperm count is low, an extraordinary process occurs. Up until this time the woman has been looking to the man for reassurance that he still loves her. She feels she has let him down.

Now, in a split second, she realises it is 'not her fault'. Relief floods through her. She will not need reassurance anymore.

At the same time, a bomb drops on the man. He has been good at reassuring his wife that he loves her. He knows she desperately wants a baby. She has said so over and over again. Now he knows that the reason she is not getting the one thing she really wants is 'his fault'!

Immediately he will look at his wife with fear in his heart, and immediately he needs reassurance from her that it is OK. Does she still love me? Can we work this through?

If you are the woman, you must watch yourself at this point. The future of your marriage is at stake.

The best way to deal with this scenario is to have made sure you have talked about it before. Express how you would feel whichever way the test comes out. Do not let it take you by surprise. This way, any mistake you make in the heat of the moment can be nullified by your previous well-expressed words.

If you are the man, you will probably have a tendency to want to avoid talking about it beforehand. This will be a mistake. Get a grip on yourself and make sure all things are well thought through, spoken out and clear. Tell each other that you love one another, that there is no blame involved, and that you will work it through together . . . whichever way it goes. If your partner has not said the words you feel you want to have heard, prompt them. Say, 'So, would you blame me if my sperm count was low?'

If she says, 'Yes!' then you have problems! But at least they are out in the open.

Listen guys. I know it's hard. But it is worth the effort. I have had a sperm test. It was not low. But it was the most useful thing in the world to have faced the possibility that it might have been.

Peer Pressure

If a woman feels pressure from society in general, then a man's main source is from his peers. The way this is expressed does depend on which cultural group a man belongs to. But, whether it is at the golf club, in the pub or on the fishing boat, WOW can they be insensitive!

We were recently at a conference in the USA. During the first session we were each asked to stand and 'Tell us about yourselves! You know, tell us about your wife, your kids, your pastimes!' One after the other told of Cheryls and Bonnies to whom they had been married for 3, 7, 15 or 20 years. They spouted about their children and got out the photos from their wallets. Now we are not sensitive about being childless (or single – and there were two or three single folk at the conference) but this was a difficult situation!

We did not want to say baldly, 'Actually we are childless!' Anyone hearing that would instantly think, 'They have a problem with this.'

Nor did we have anything that important to say when it came to our turn. And how Sharon was supposed to tell everyone about 'her wife' I was not quite sure!

This kind of situation repeats on the one-to-one level over and over again. The basic male group dynamic includes introductions, telling stories, laughing at each other's jokes, and then breaking into pairs to chat a bit more intimately. Nine times out of ten this one-to-one conversation will start with, 'Do you have family?'.

I would not mind so much about that if an answer of, 'No' was ever sufficient. Or even, 'Yes, Sharon and I!' But it always seems to go on into, 'So why's that?' 'Which of you has the difficulty?', 'What are you doing about it?', 'Are you going to adopt?' To be honest, by the time I have been through this process with a couple of members of the group I am a bit bored of the subject and would like to talk about something else.

Of course I want to be enthusiastic about their children. But most times all they do is tell me their names, ages and say, 'They're doing really well!' and then drop the subject. I seem to have to talk more about children I don't have – and, as a result, don't have any interest in – than they do about real living breathing human beings.

MALE COMPETITION

Beyond the friendly interest of male peers there is the dangerous world of competitiveness and agressive one-upmanship.

An extreme example of this happened while we were on holiday in Tenerife. Very foolishly we submitted to the torture of a time-share presentation. We partly went for the amusement, partly for the free tickets to the water park.

Everything was going smoothly until the salesman realised we had no intention of buying and our only interest was in his sales technique. At this he became abusive. He swore and cajoled. He teased and fidgeted.

At first we thought this was funny. Then suddenly he turned towards me, opened his legs, and said, 'This is your problem!'

He seemed to stare. He was playing a power game. To be honest we did not know what he was getting at.

'No balls! That's your problem! You've got no balls!'

At this he grabbed his own testicles.

Quite a sight!

Gladly I had had my sperm test only a few weeks before and could put him straight.

How I would have felt if my sperm count was low, I am not so sure

Another example comes from a friend of ours.

He and his wife were going through investigations relating to infertility. He went for a sperm test and the results were a shock. His count was so low that the doctors said it would take a miracle for him to father a child.

This news almost destroyed him.

But life goes on. After a short while he was in work feeling low. One of his colleagues asked him what the problem was. Very foolishly he told them, 'in confidence'. Talking was good. He was getting it out of his system. But what he did not know was that he was also setting himself up for a hard time.

First thing the next morning he walked into work.

'I hear you're a Jaffa Pete!' he heard someone say. Looking up he saw the grinning face of one of his 'friends'.

'Eh?'.

'Ya know, No pips!! Jaffa, no pips! Got it?'

Not so funny when you think about it, is it?

So started an awful few weeks of being reminded again and again of something which was already hurting him at a depth that he could not handle.

There is a time to speak, and a time to stay silent!

*   *   *

So the man can have a rough time too. Often he needs more support than is offered. It can be a very lonely time and it is important to be well informed in order to be ready to cope. Christian bookshelves are filled – at present – with books about male psychology. If you want more on this subject we suggest you pick up a couple of publications, and explore. But more than that, you need some good friends about you, on whom you can off-load after a particularly bad day.

EIGHT

MIND MATTERS

M ost childless people will tell you that, if they were able to live in a world of their own, without any advice or comment, coping would be far easier. Small difficulties can become major problems when mixed with misguided advice or comments from others. The aim of this chapter is to explore some of these comments and get your defences ready.

Fore-warned is fore-armed.

There are two things that are certain in this world: Firstly, if you are hurting, you will be extra-sensitive to everything people say. And secondly, people will say it anyway!

As Christians we have some extra help. We know we are not here to fulfil everyone else's expectations, or even our own. We only have to seek to fulfil God's purposes for our lives. As a result we can, if we do our thinking beforehand, arm ourselves with the right kind of attitudes to help diffuse the destructive effects of some of these jibes.

The battle is to maintain *peace of mind* in a world of well-meaning interfering whatsits. This can be achieved if we let God teach us how he sees things and there-fore arm ourselves with the mental, emotional and spir-itual weapons that he offers. Let us show you what we mean.

The first weapon we would like to introduce is:

THE JESUS FILTER

This is designed for when someone you love – and who loves you – offers you well-meaning advice. Respect for them leaves you wanting to be open to what they say. After all you cannot ignore everyone.

However, just because someone loves you does not necessarily mean they will understand your feelings. Those who are close to you also have their own worries, struggles and longings. Maybe they want you to have children so that they can have a grandchild or niece/nephew. They can therefore push too hard and leave you feeling guilty. They may not realise the stress you are under, and therefore how exhausted you feel by the whole thing.

Here is a suggested course of action.

The key is to **listen** to what they say. **Smile** at them and maintain good **eye contact**. If anything is unclear, ask them to **clarify** it. If necessary **take a note** on a piece of paper – as this can show them that you are taking them seriously. But whatever you do, **do not react** or even try and respond in any way at the time. **Thank** them for caring, and tell them you will **go away and think about** what they have said.

All the above process helps to maintain relationships with the people who are most important in your life, while still giving you the right and opportunity to accept or reject what they have to say. This is vital if you are to remain happy, and happiness is one of the greatest resources you have for coping with the stress of the situation you are in.

But what about later?

Later you take a moment to analyse what was said to you. You could do this by yourself, but it would be better to do it together with your wife or husband (NB: this kind of pressure can be put on women or men).

Before you start you must go through another simple exercise: Consciously remind yourself (or one another) to **separate the advice from the person who gave it**. The person is someone who loves and cares for you. After all, that was the only reason for them bothering to try and get involved. The advice is now an inanimate object that you can analyse, use, partially use or destroy, without writing off your friend or relative.

Next, ask, '**is this what Jesus would say to us?**'

Again, it can be useful to jot down some notes. You can

make three headings. '**Yes**' – for all those things that Jesus definitely would say to you. '**No**' – for all those things he definitely would not say to you. And '**not sure**' – for those in between.

This can be a fascinating process. You will normally find a good dose of all three in any well-meaning advice. If you do not go through this process it is easy to react against the bad, and therefore miss out on the good. Often you will find that God has spoken to you in the midst of what you felt was a most destructive or manipulative time with a loved one.

For example, imagine someone said this to you:

> 'Darling, you know I love you. And you know I don't want to interfere, but . . . I really do think you have given up too soon. I have known you a long time, and I know you have a tendency, when faced with something very difficult and personal, to put your head in the sand and pretend it will go away. You will never forgive yourself if you don't try everything possible. So, why not try another doctor and ask if there are any more tests they can do. I always thought the other one was incompetent. He may have said there was no hope, but I just don't believe it. After all, genetically it doesn't make sense.'

Can you see the mixture of the good, the bad and the ugly. Can you also see how asking, 'Would Jesus have said that?' helps you work out which is which?

So, on to our second weapon . . .

THE BLOWOUT

There are actions to go with this weapon. Please do the following even as you read:

1. Imagine yourself looking a piece of rotten advice, hurtful comment or ignorant bigotry straight in the face.
2. Inhale a good lungful of air.

3. Place your tongue between your lips, closing them firmly around your tongue.
4. Exhale all the air you have through your mouth making the appropriate noise.

Another name for this weapon is '*THE JESUS RASPBERRY*'. It is extremely effective at banishing any destructive effects of a 'comment'. It also has the habit of making a '*Jesus raspberry blower*' feel a whole lot better, without them needing to kick a door or punch someone's eyes out.

Our only further advice is this. **You have no need to put the comment-maker right!** Getting your own heart right is the far greater and – at least in the short term – your only priority. So, the comment-maker does not need to be in the room when you give their comment the raspberry! In fact, what makes a Jesus raspberry one better than a raspberry by itself, is that it starts with Jesus, who on the cross said, 'Father FORGIVE THEM, for they do not understand what they are doing!' Start by taking this attitude. Then consciously pray, even aloud, this prayer. Then, in your mind, separate the comment from the person. Then raspberry it! From now on you need not let it have any hold on the way you think or feel.

Now we have outlined how to fight against destructive questions/comments that some people make, the next step is to take a good look at what those comments are likely to be. It is important to do this now because in a moment of tension it is very hard to think straight. It is therefore better to have done your thinking before when you have time to examine yourself, your situation and how this comment relates to you. We must realise that these comments would not be made unless they were partly correct in some situations. The reason generalisations are so hurtful is that you feel pigeon-holed. You feel like you are being treated as a case that needs solving rather than the unique person you are.

Our aim is to list a series of phrases or situations and give you a chance to jot down how this relates to you. Then, should they occur in your life, instead of flying into a rage or bursting into tears, you may be able to – maybe still with a few tears or some anger – explain rationally how you feel.

Here we go:

1. **'Do you have any family?'**
   This is a tricky one! From the questioner's point of view it is an innocent enquiry into whether you have children. To you it instantly makes the statement that you – a couple without children – are not 'a real family'. In a culture where 'family life' is meant to be highly valued (although a few moments of sober reflection will tell you that it is being less valued by the day) this feels like an attack both on you and on your extended 'family' relationships. It is important to note that this is *not* an *attack* question! You will seem very odd if you reply with a defensive, 'What makes a family a "family" anyway?'

   Take your *time* and reply, adding the appropriate correction. For *example* you could say, 'If you mean, "Do you have any *children*?", then the answer's, "No!"' For others you may *even* go as far as adding, 'It appears we are infertile.'

   The effect of this will be to give the questioner a few things to think about, so give them time to reorganise their thoughts. Do not *expect* them, without a pause, to be able to come out with the most sensitive caring remark ever.

   We have a little trick to *help* us deal with this situation. We treat it as a game. The moment someone asks the question we begin to smile inside and to take notes on how our friend deals with the gentle wobbly we are about to throw. The effect is that we relax and become more gentle. Any sense of antagonism disappears, and it becomes an opportunity for us to chat with them and to learn from one another.

2. **'Are you sure?'**
Anyone who knows anything about infertility would
not ask this question. Instead they would enquire as
to how long you have been trying to get pregnant.
As we have seen (in chapter 5) the medical profession
usually defines infertilty as having had unprotected
sex for at least one year without have conceived.
This does not necessarily mean that a couple who is
defined as infertile are incapable of ever conceiving.
Many couples who have been trying unsuccessfully to
get pregnant between 6 and 18 months, go on to have
children without any medical intervention. The normal
state of a couple defined as infertile is that the doctors
'have a theory' as to why they are not conceiving. Only
a very few couples are ever told, 'You will never have
children!'

Suffice it to say, **this question is not meant as an
attack!** Ninety-nine per cent of the time the person
asking is merely ignorant of the facts above. They
do not deserve a mouthful and it will not serve your
purpose to give them one. It would be far better to
respond by giving them the facts of how long you
have been trying, and any advice or explanations the
doctors have passed on to you. If there is a tendency
in you to be upset by people not understanding, then
you can now mobilise that energy and divert it into
a longing to educate. After all, you cannot condemn
someone for not being informed if you have not taken
the opportunity to help them learn.

3. **'Whose fault is it?'** or, put another way,
'Which of you is it that has the problem?'
There are two keys to this situation. Firstly, keep in mind
that any difficulty in having children is a problem that
couples have. An apportioning of blame is ridiculous.
None of us have control over our own reproductive
organs and anyway in marriage the two have become 'one
flesh' (Gen 2:24). Any physical problem that our partners
have should be seen to be as much ours as theirs.

Secondly, answer the question in as matter of fact a way as possible without betraying the trust of your partner or extended family. There really is no point in ramming the above thinking down your questioner's throat. Give them the facts as they stand. If they then continue with this line of enquiry, you may make some comment along the lines of, 'We don't really see it as a matter of "fault" either way.' This should open up a whole new line of discussion, and may give you a chance to share with them the Christian understanding of marriage.

4. **'Yes, we are looking forward to our first grandchild'**
   Parents – even when they love you and you love them – can be one of the biggest pressures on those who are childless. The reason is that they may have developed an interesting skill: making their point *indirectly!*
   We know a mother who is an expert at this. When her daughter-in-law was getting into a car which her son was borrowing for a few days she was heard to say, 'It's a very good car to drive while you are pregnant, as there is lots of room behind the steering wheel!' The son and daughter-in-law were in the process of discovering whether they were infertile!
   There are no quick solutions to the issue of parent– child relationships. Freud made a career out of assuming that all of mankind's problems start there. In some situations the answer is to confront, and ask the parent to at least speak openly. In others it is better to ignore, as a confrontation may only make matters worse. Most families lurch between a combination of the two. The younger couple, in the end, must work out what they are going to do together with the Lord. The potential grandparents must be patient, loving and involved when given permission. Most of all, do not let your emotions destroy the relationship. Do not say, 'I'm never talking to you again!' Be angry – if appropriate – but leave the door open.

5. **'Here! Take her/him! . . .'**
This is Aunty & Uncle territory. When your sister
or a close friend has a baby they can get all sym-
pathetic towards you. This can come out either by
them always keeping the child out of your way, or,
more usually, they keep thrusting the offspring into
your arms, 'because you won't have one of your
own'.

It has to be said that our family is very good in
this area. However, we have an infertile couple who
are friends of ours for whom this is a real problem.
They both come from big families. They say that
family reunions can be 'a nightmare'. Everybody is
either standing back or thrusting children at them.
Hopefully soon they will adopt and the problem will
go away. Until then they have to go through mental
preparation before getting out of the car!

6. **'Why have sex any more?'**
The old prayer book marriage service should be banned!
Sorry if you are attached to seventeenth-century English,
but it has a major problem written into it. During the
service something is read out which says: 'Marriage is
given, *first* for the conceiving, bearing and nurturing of
children; *second* for mutual support through life; and
third for the enjoyment and fulfilment of one another
through the sexual bond' (our emphasis).

These three are clearly part of marriage; but whatever
got into them to put it in that order? Many people
are married without children, so it cannot be the
primary purpose of marriage. Genesis 2 gives the
impression that it is that 'the two would become one'
that is *first*. The production of children is *secondary*, and
unnecessary. Sex has a place even without conception or
birth of another generation. Spiritually, psychologically
and physically a man and woman find a unity and
expression of love through the sexual act. PLEASE, do
not let this be stolen from you just because you cannot
have children.

7. **'Why don't you marry someone else?'**
The painful part of this comment is that it regularly will
come from the partner who has a physical reason for not
being fertile – if you know that it is one of you or the
other. It is easy to understand. They love their spouse.
They know that he/she desperately wants children, and
they see the reason that their loved one is unable to have
offspring is the fact that he/she is married to them. So
they ask the question.

But don't be fooled! This is not a genuine suggestion.
Nor is it a statement of permission. It is exactly the
opposite. It is a challenge!

It could be best translated, 'Do you love me enough
to love me even though I am stopping you having
your own children?' Put that way it's obvious what
you should do. If you hear this question you must
reply strongly and confidently, 'I want no one else but
you.' Any hesitation will breed mistrust; and, even if
you don't want it to, that could be the first crack in a
marriage which had been strong to that point!

So, hear the words within the words. Always listen
for feelings. All people are canny when they are hurting.
Straight questions never tell you what you want to
know – so find out some other way. It is difficult days
like the one when this question is asked that show you
to be a really great lover, or just out to get what you
want from your partner.

8. **'Do we really want children anyway?'**
Another tricky question. Again there is a hidden agenda.
The difficulty here is that this is really **a request for
permission to be happy even if you never have
children**. However, there are still some bigger issues
around.

If you say 'No! We don't really want children' the
question will come back, 'Why have we been doing
what we've been doing? We've been trying to have children. Would you have been upset if we had succeeded?'

Alternatively, a reply of, 'But of course we want

children' fails to give permission for happiness; and, particularly if it is your partner who has the physical difficulty, can leave them in a depression.

The only solution is to try and say two things together. 'Of course we would be happy if we had children. We've been trying and we would be overjoyed if we succeeded.' And, 'However, we are happy now! And we have each other. No infertility can take that away from us. After all, right now, as a result of our difficulties, we still have so much time, and the rare opportunity to keep making choices. It may not be our first choice, but let's rejoice in what we do have.' The important thing is to get these out quickly and together. Then, as you chat, you can expand both. It may take time, but it will be worth it.

9. **'Would you like us to pray for you?'**
Part of the last chapter was about this, but we did not feel this list would be complete without it. After all, this question is probably the one which puts the biggest psychological pressure on a Christian couple who are infertile. There are some wonderful stories of God doing miracles and babies being born. There are also tragedies, where couples went on hoping and hoping, and gave up their opportunities to explore other options.

The comment above can come from well-meaning people to any couple anywhere along the process. Our guidelines would fall into three categories:

a) If **you** hear from the Lord that he wants to do a miracle for you, then let anyone pray for you who is willing and expect God to act. Reassess this every few months to make sure it is not just your wishful thinking.

b) If you have not heard personally from the Lord, and both you and your partner are happy and feeling strong enough today to put up with a 'being prayed for' session — together with questions and suggestions of what might be 'the cause' — then go for it!

c) If you or your partner are *not* happy about it, say, 'Thank you for offering. Yes please pray for us as this is a hard time. But we would rather you pray for us without us present if you don't mind. We can get quite emotional, and God can hear your prayers whether we are there or not. Thank you again.' And then walk away.

d) Alternatively, you could say, 'No thank you! It really isn't any of your business.' You may think this is hard, but we have sometimes felt very odd when people asked to pray for us. After all sex and procreation are something very intimate. It should be just you, your partner and God involved. How dare anyone else invite themselves into the process. It can almost feel like being spiritually raped! So if you feel that way, say so.

10. **'If you'd just relax . . . ?'**
Aaagh! Yes you are right. This is the 'It's all in the mind' jibe. It is so frustrating to hear even doctors say this kind of thing. It gets your goat and makes you anything but relaxed!

However (and you knew we had to say this), your mental state can affect your fertility. If there are no other obvious physical causes for not conceiving then the 'try relaxing' approach has something going for it. Sometimes when people move house; or get the job they have always wanted; or go on holiday; something is released. It is difficult to assess afterwards what it is that 'happened'. The only problem is that 'trying' to relax normally achieves the opposite.

One suggestion might be to give the person who says this to you a good mouthful about what you think of their comment. You may find this is so relaxing that it has the desired effect!?

11. **'So you're a career woman?'**
Being misunderstood is part of being human. We all know there are debates about whether women should be at home or at work in the media and politics. This is

a good chance to be relieved that at least they can't be angry with you for not being at home – which would probably be the case if you did have children. You also have the opportunity to argue the case for women with careers and children, and just when they are getting a little heated, drop the fact that you are childless. It will probably be a learning experience for them!

Finally, in this chapter, we want to include something that Chris and Mary Key put together while they were really suffering, longing and failing to have children. It is a list of 'Dos and Don'ts' for those who are family or friends of subfertile couples. If you are like us – not too worried about it all and preferring if people keep their noses out – these suggestions may seem a bit emotional. But it is a resource put together by Christian leaders who, at the time, were breaking their hearts in prayer to have children and desperately wanted support. So it gives a good balance to our own approach:

Do's and Don'ts for Family and Friends of Childless Couples

DON'T   *assume* that they want children and can't have them.

DON'T   pry until you know them well enough.

DO   encourage them to share their needs for prayer.

DO   help them to express their feelings and even to cry.

DON'T   make promises for God that they will have children unless certain that God has told you.

DON'T   always talk on this single topic. They'd like to be treated as normal people sometimes.

DON'T   come out with over-simple advice. (I'm afraid we got sick of people saying 'just relax' and 'you're young yet'!)

DON'T   condemn them for times of doubt or anger.

DO   try *to* put them in touch with people in a similar situation *if they say they want you to.*

DON'T   unnaturally avoid talking about children in their company or try to 'spare them the agony' of being with children. The pain doesn't vanish if youngsters are out of sight.

DO   assure them occasionally of your prayers (and then pray!).

DO   let them have *their* feelings. Some are upset, others not, others in-between. Not everyone is exactly like us and we must not impose how we would feel on them.

DO   assure them of your appreciation of them as people.

DON'T   go on saying 'God is giving you more time to serve Him' or 'Just wait till you have the problems children bring'. That may be true, but it is very unhelpful. (After all, why would anyone have children if this were the case!)

DON'T   overdo the sympathy, but . . .

DO   try and spot the moment when they want to talk about it.

DON'T   feel you always have to say something helpful. Usually listening and caring is enough.

DON'T   forget the husband's needs.

DON'T   always expect (or promise) instant results from prayer.

DO   stick with them, whatever happens.

DON'T   underestimate the powerful emotions involved.

DON'T   discount God's intervention!

THE MAYBE SYNDROME

In only a very few cases of apparent infertility is it possible for the doctors to say that it is absolutely impossible for the couple to have a baby. Examples include when a man has no testicles or a woman no womb. In most other circumstances there is a possibility, even if that possibility includes some kind of medical involvement – either ethical or unethical. Couples ask, 'Is there any way we can have a baby?' Doctors reply, 'Probably not, but MAYBE.'

This will normally leave a childless couple with a major problem. How do they know when they should give up hope, and get on with their lives? We call this the 'maybe syndrome'.

In our case the 'maybe syndrome' has worked like this. We have been through the basic investigations so that we can be as sure as possible that we are not going to damage ourselves (e.g. ectopic pregnancies, etc). Nobody can tell why I am not pregnant, but the temperature charts do give some indications. We enjoy being able to make love without contraception. We would not mind if a child suddenly appeared. The doctors say it may happen. But we have decided to live our lives on the basis that it is not going to happen. Most of all we are determined not to live 'if only' lives. The alternative is to keep on hoping. Those who take this view have to be prepared to keep their lives on hold, just in case they get pregnant.

Every month the last few days tick by – 23, 24, 25, 26, 27. Every month the hope begins to rise. Will the period start or not? There are other tasks to be done. 'But,' they think, 'why do them until we know?'

Then the trickle of blood appears. Total disappointment again. Grief strikes. The next few days are for mourning. Until the end of your period.

Then it's back into action. Hoping . . . hoping . . . holding your breath . . .

It's endless. And can be for almost 30 years!

However you look at it, it's torture. In our opinion the first option seems to lead to a more relaxed and productive lifestyle.

So there are two ways of mentally approaching the on-going experience of being infertile:

1. We're going to keep hoping and praying no matter how small the chances.
2. We're going to leave it in God's hands and devote our energy into serving him in this world.

Both positions can be sustained from the Bible. But we believe the second is a more New Testament approach. 'Seek first the kingdom of God' and let other things fall into place as God directs.

WHEN TO DECIDE

The next question is when do you decide you must adopt one of these positions – or another of your own devising?
　　May we suggest three answers:

1.　**When you want to.**
　　You have to be happy with your own decision or you will worry and chaff at the bit.

2.　**When seeking a child clearly begins to conflict with 'Seeking first the kingdom of God and his righteousness'.**
　　You can only serve one master. You either serve God or your desire to have a baby. If a conflict arises you know the choice you have to make.

3.　**When ethical medical options have run out.**
　　The medical world is continually coming up with new treatments and techniques to help the infertile. During the time a couple attends consultations at a clinic they may be offered an assortment of these options. The first thing to do is to carefully check through the ethics of what is being suggested and if necessary get expert advice. This is normally forthcoming from both Christians and non-Christians.
　　If you believe a technique offered is morally OK, both medically and financially, then we suggest you should go for it! You only live once, and you will certainly regret it if you do not at least try! But there comes a time when the infertility clinic may say they have run out of suggestions. From then on it becomes just a matter of will you get pregnant this month. There is nothing particular you can do about it.

In this case stop worrying or, if possible, even think-
ing about it. Start the process of letting the dream die!
Then, if it should jump back out of the grave, PRAISE
GOD and enjoy it! If not, then let it stay buried.

You may be saying that all seems a bit too simple. 'It is all
very well saying, "Let it die." But I don't know how.'
   That is the subject of the next chapter. How do you let
your dreams die when you have decided you have to?

NINE

HOPE DEAD?

Blessed are those who mourn for they will be comforted.
(Matt 5:4)

Living hope and dead hope are easier to handle than 'hope deferred'. 'Hope deferred makes the heart sick' (Prov 13:12).

There comes a point where any childless couple either gets pregnant or, deep down, they begin to know that it is not going to happen. Those in this latter position may not yet admit that they have given up, but at the root of their being – rightly or wrongly – the belief that they will never have a baby has become established.

The problem is that the way we act, talk and think does not always reflect what we actually believe. Nowhere is this more clearly seen than when a person is bereaved. I remember clearly when I was told that a dearly loved aunt had died. The first thing I did was laugh. It did not make sense. It was just that I did not know how to handle the feelings I was feeling. Laughter was the only way I knew to let out the pressure.

Seeing your hopes of having a baby slipping away is just like being bereaved. A death has occurred. Not the death of a living child. Rather the death of the child that might have been. Some find themselves reacting just as if the child had been born and then died. They move into a classic bereavement cycle. (See fig 1.)

Maybe you recognise yourself in one these stages. Maybe

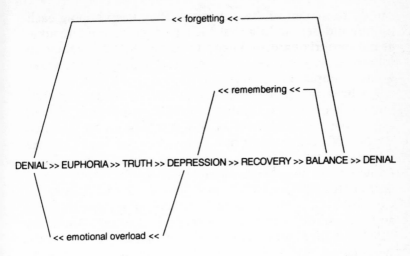

Figure 1

you have just returned to one of them for the third or fourth time. If you have, you are not unusual. The process of grief is one of God's design features put into human beings to help them cope with the traumas of life.

Let's go through it in detail:

Denial

Physical symptoms: swallowing, shaking, cold, numb.
This is a strange mental state. The person concerned knows that something they really do not want to happen has happened. They then bury that in their mind and think, speak, even live their lives on the basis that it has not happened. A mild form of this is when you give someone bad news and they instantly say, 'It's not true!' as if that would make it go away.

In the area of infertility it may be that a man has an extremely low sperm count, or a woman has badly damaged tubes. At one level of their personality they know the information they have received leaves nearly zero hope of conceiving. But they keep asking the doctor what they can do to maximise their chances. They keep hoping each month and demanding that their partner have intercourse at inappropriate times. Each time a period arrives they go into a depression saying 'It's not fair. I really thought it was going to happen this month.'

A Christian version of this situation is someone who has already been to 20 or 30 different healing meetings. Whenever a new preacher arrives in town they go for personal prayer. When they meet him or her they will say, 'God has promised me a child. It's been a long time coming but I know he will answer your prayers. I have faith, you know.' Our analysis of this is that they certainly do not have faith. Certainly not faith as the Bible describes. Instead they are suffering under a bad case of misplaced wishful thinking. Maybe if they genuinely cried out to God he would do what he has done so many times before: a miracle. But the behaviour described above is better understood when it is seen as an extreme case of saying something is true in the hope that that will make it true.

Euphoria

People in denial can regularly be radiant with happiness. They have forced themselves to believe that all they hope for is true. So obviously they are wonderfully happy. Of course they are living in wonderland. But why not? If everything you have been dreading has now happened, why not escape in your mind into a place where it has not happened. You would be very sad in the real world and it is more fun being happy than sad. So make up a pretend world where you can be happy. More importantly, it is easier to cope when you are happy. So, if you are in danger of total emotional collapse, it is safer for your brain to fool you into believing something that will make you happy. Then when the risk of damage is past, it can slowly let the truth back into your system. Quite clever really!

Most cases of denial are somewhere between the two described above. A little self-analysis of how you are reacting to bad news will show you your version. The moment you are aware of doing it, just coax yourself back into truth. It may not be so relaxing, but it means you can get yourself organised for what is really ahead.

Truth

Of course a person's mind knows there are dangers with believing in an unreal world – the real world will continue to go on around them. For example it may be safe to drive on the right hand side of the road as long as nothing comes the other way. But sooner or later you must get back on the left (in England!). Sooner is preferable!

If you are trying to help someone who is in denial, then your job is to gently and safely help them bring the truth back into vision. Most importantly, do not get angry with them. The reason they are doing what they are doing is to escape emotional trauma. You must communicate by the way you interact with them that there is less trauma in knowing the truth than staying in denial. Do not think they have to confront it all in one go. Let them get there one step at a time. Also, do not think you have to give them the information. In most cases they already know the truth. It is your job to help them unbury it.

Depression

Possible physical symptoms:
pain/sickness
stress expressed through areas e.g.: back, colon, legs, head
sweats and dizziness
changes in eating and sleeping patterns – eating too much or too little, restlessness, distressing dreams, inability to go to sleep, waking early, fear of sleep
tiredness – hallucinations and dreams

Possible emotional symptoms:
talking and crying – anguish, longing – repeating the situation over and over again

depending on others – asking for help in decision-making
or handing decisions over to others
anger and frustration with self and others over trivial
things
apathy – lack of interest and respect – loss of identity,
status.
guilt – irrational or justified
anger/resentment – why us? why me? how could they
do this?
sadness or acute loneliness
stigma of loss/lack – tendency to isolation

Dangers:
The signs of this phase are not acceptance but endurance.
You can tell when things are improving when a few small
decisions begin to be made, or things begin to get done.

The problem with the truth in these cases is that the person
sees it as insurmountable bad news. So euphoria is soon
replaced by one of the many forms of depression. If this
depression is too severe then the person will instantly revert
to denial and the process starts again.

The normal thing to happen is that the demands of
everyday life play a part in diverting the power of the bad
feelings associated with confronting the truth. The person
gets on sorting out some practical things. With their mind
distracted they come back to emotional balance.

Balance

They then cope quite well for a while and begin to believe
that everything is all right really. They can handle the
problem. It is not such a big deal. They may even mutter,
'It's not as bad as I was saying.' Notice something? Yes, they
have moved back into denial. They are happy, but they are
covering up.

Then suddenly they see a photograph of a baby. Truth
strikes them. Down into depression and a pool of tears.
And the process starts again.

Gradually the cycles become less acute. Each time you

go around a piece of history goes by and your emotions become less strained. Sometimes the process needs a helping hand.

WHAT INHIBITS US FROM HEALING?

Advancing through the process of grief is very painful. Grief evokes in us frustration, sadness, loneliness, guilt, regret, anxiety, anguish or despair. All of these are extremely uncomfortable feelings, often as painful as any physical pain. We would rather avoid it than go through it. Grief initiates transitions which involve a conscious recognition of loss, acknowledgement of the way life now is, and acceptance of the need to develop a new sense of identity. Confrontation with one's sense of self and the challenge to build a new perspective is both painful and involves much hard work.

DOES GOD UNDERSTAND GRIEF?

Not only does the Bible include passages about grief in general terms (e.g.: 1 Sam 15:11; Luke 6:21; John 16:20, and, indirectly, Luke 2:35) but also it has specific passages about the grief of those who are experiencing infertility. 'I am a woman who is deeply troubled. . . . I have been praying here out of my great anguish and grief' (1 Sam 1:15,16).

These are the words of Hannah who, before she received the miracle of conceiving a baby – Samuel – was found weeping on the steps of the Temple. The priest, Eli, thought she was drunk. She knew otherwise. She was grieving over her infertility.

POSSIBLE ACTIVITY TO HELP ADVANCE THE PROCESS

Depending on the severity of the grief symptoms you are experiencing you may be able to chat to a family member or a good friend. If this is enough for you or your partner then go for it, remembering that grief ebbs and flows like the tides. It may fade away until we think it has gone. But then it floods back with a vengeance and we can be fooled into thinking that no progress has been made and we are back to square one.

So keep in mind there are other options. Maybe this list of suggestions might help:

TALK TO:
- **each other (i.e. your husband or wife)**
- **a friend or family member**
- **a member or leader at your local Christian church**. Most churches can offer some form of grief counselling. It may be a strange request for you to ask for grief counselling for infertility, but they should get the idea.
- **someone (or a group) who are going through the same things**. This kind of thing is being set up by many evangelical Christian churches at the moment. Alternatively you could contact the various adoption agencies (listed at the end of chapter 11).
- **a professional grief counsellor**. Again a Christian church may have someone trained in this way, or be able to recommend a Christian counsellor who is local. *Do not* just take a name out of the newspaper. There are some charlatans around, as well as occultists and hypnotists, who are putting themselves forward as some kind of accredited counsellors. If your church cannot help, either contact your GP or CARE for the Family.

The key word to it all is TALK!

And when you have done talking, begin to make the decisions needed to deal with the rest of your life!

A FUNERAL?

One of the methods that might help you to advance the mourning process is symbolism. If you had given birth to a child and they had then died, you would have had a funeral. Similar meaningful acts are now recommended to

those who experience miscarriages. So why not put together
a form of funeral for your dreams and hopes of the child that
never was.

We have to say that we would find what we are about
to suggest quite bizarre. From our perspective, 'meaningful
acts' have a habit of being more humorous than meaningful.
If you feel the same way, then read these next few para-
graphs and laugh. But, in our experience, there are many
people who are helped by the kind of suggestion below. If
so, go for it!

Plant a rose in your back garden
When you are ready, arrange for a short ceremony. You
might write some poetry or a song. You might create a
picture that represents your dream of having a child. You
could burn the picture you have made and put the ashes
on the ground around the rose.

You could do this with just the two of you. Alternatively
you might like to ask a Christian leader from your church to
come and help you; maybe even invite others, like friends
and family. The purpose of what you are going to do is to
symbolise letting your dreams die. Sometimes doing this in
public helps you to stick to the decisions you have made.

Obviously you do not do this until you are sure you can
let the dream of bearing children go. But once you have, it
is helpful to be able to put a date and time to it!

Jesus said, 'Blessed are those who mourn, for they shall
be comforted' (Matt 5:4).

HOW LONG, O LORD, HOW LONG

According to grief counsellors the average time it takes for
the extreme symptoms to settle following the death of a
close relative is 18 months to two years. From our research
we would suggest that a similar figure relates well to the
grief after giving up hope that you will ever have a baby.

One husband told us of his grief. He has a very low sperm
count. His wife has a hormonal imbalance that means she is
not in the least broody. She did not ever desperately feel a

need for children and has just got on with a rather brilliant career. He, on the other hand, always dreamed that he would hold his own children and see them grow up. He has a wonderfully nurturing personality.

He told us that from the day he knew they would never have a child he cried every day for 18 months. He got on with things, but he was very very sad. The cycle described above would have been his experience on an almost hourly basis at the beginning.

Even now, a number of years later, he will cry whenever something comes up to remind him. 'The grief never goes away. It just becomes part of you,' he said, as he sat in our living room a year ago, with tears gently trickling over his half-smiling cheeks. The most important thing is that you do feel it, he continued 'What's the point in being human if you never let yourself feel what you are feeling?' We agree! Feeling things, and letting the pressure out through tears is all part of how God created human beings: made in the image of God (Luke 19:41; John 11:35).

TEN

MISCARRIAGE AND STILL BIRTH

In the last chapter we made a brief reference to miscarriage as a particular kind of bereavement. It can also be one of the most awful experiences and memories of those who still remain childless. This book would not be complete without something specifically written about the feelings and thoughts surrounding becoming pregnant . . . and then, suddenly, not being pregnant anymore.

This is not just a difficulty for women. The fathers are often overlooked when sympathy is given. Sometimes, emotionally, things can be even worse for them.

A very large proportion of women have miscarriages. Most with their first pregnancy. But quite a few have a miscarriage even after having had one baby.

Professor Winston, in his book, *Getting Pregnant*,[1] estimates that as many as 23 per cent of all human pregnancies miscarry. This sounds very high, but takes into account all those that happen in the first few days after the embryo tries to attach itself to the uterine lining. If a miscarriage then happens, the woman concerned will have her period as normal and may not even be aware she was ever pregnant.

Some women do feel pregnant when they are and this can be an indication. But most doctors say that self-diagnosis is notoriously unreliable. It is a myth to say we can feel what is going on in our own bodies; at least until the symptoms become more obvious.

WHY?

The main reasons for a miscarriage are to do with the development of the baby, as extreme malformation of a foetus normally ends in a miscarriage. This is a natural process that is occurring, letting the child go with as little suffering as possible.

However, there are some more complex causes which we have listed below.

Some Causes of Miscarriage:

a. Genetic Abnormalities e.g.:
    • Three chromosomes of one type (instead of a normal pair)
    • One X chromosome missing
    • Multiple or extra chromosomes
    • Changes in individual chromosomes

b. Hydatidiform Mole. This abnormality causes a placenta to develop, but no child. This happens in only 1 in every 2,000 pregnancies, and is probably inherited from the mother's (or even father's) parents.

c. Age. The older a woman becomes, the more likely that she will produce an abnormal ovum.

d. Hormonal Problems. There are a variety of problems that can fit into this category. For example, some women do not produce enough progesterone, which is the hormone (produced both by the ovary – in a normal cycle – and the placenta – after pregnancy starts) which stops the woman having her period. However, doctors are still debating whether the low progesterone level produces a miscarriage, or the other way around!

e. Abnormalities in the Tubes, Uterus, Cervix, etc. This could be a long-term defect, or one that only happens when a particular pregnancy starts, for example a failure of blood supply from the uterus or chemical deficiency.

f. Environmental Hazards. This can be on a large or small scale. Dioxin (as in a chemical disaster in Italy), radiation (as around Chernobyl), some insecticides, etc are typical of world scale problems. However smoking, food poisoning (particularly from undercooked eggs or products like soft cheese), certain drugs (like Thalidomide), marijuana or alcohol can all cause miscarriage in some women.

g. Infections. Anything from flu to more notorious bacteria or viruses can cause problems.

h. Immunological Matters. Both the woman and the baby's body have a system that produces antibodies. The purpose of this is to fight disease. Sadly sometimes the antibodies do damage to the mother or baby.

i. Psychological Factors. Although difficult to define, if a woman is happy and reassured she is probably less likely to miscarry.

j. Inappropriate Exercise. Although a pregnant woman must stay as fit as possible, in most cases (particularly those with a history of miscarriage) doctors will suggest taking it easy – not throwing yourself around a volley ball court – and being aware of how you feel on a particular day. In more extreme cases, total bedrest is suggested.

That is a basic outline. If you are concerned, then these are a few things you can do to reduce the risk of miscarriage:

• Rest • Eat fibre (to avoid constipation • Iron and Folic Acid tablets • Cut out smoking and alcohol • Avoid travel • Be careful making love (or stop a while!?) • No sport . . .

(There are also some more complex ways of medically treating miscarriage. If you want to know the details we once again suggest you either see your GP or get hold of Professor Winston's book, *Getting Pregnant*.)

But, PLEASE NOTE, do not blame yourself if you should miscarry. You may think that it is because you ignored one of the above that it happened. But it is never as simple as that. Some women are extra careful, and they still miscarry. When things go wrong, it can be for all sorts of reasons.

The truth is that it is very difficult to miscarry a normal healthy baby.

As we have said, many many women experience miscarriage. We know one woman who has had 13, and is still trying to have a child. My sister experienced three lost pregnancies before eventually having a healthy baby – Lauren.

However, in a book on childlessness this subject brings up a whole wealth of other issues. We therefore want to discuss a number of matters that relate to the feelings that the subject or experience of miscarriage might bring up.

THE EASIER/HARDER DEBATE

This relates to the statement sometimes aimed at a woman who has miscarried, by another woman who has never conceived.

'It's easier for you,' she says, 'at least you know you can get pregnant!'

What a thing to say! But what feelings there must be to say something like that in the first place. Suffice it to say, this kind of thing is going to be said and only rational objective assessment will be able to show how wrong it is.

'Easier' and 'harder' are such subjective words. As we have already discussed in relation to infertility in general, EVERYBODY REACTS IN THEIR OWN WAY. Some people are emotionally strong. They instantly grieve and feel all that needs to be felt. They become practical and soon move on to another chapter of their life. Others find miscarriage, even with the encouragement that they can almost certainly have another child, one of the most soul-destroying experiences ever. After all, no matter how many other children you go on to have, you love (and would have gone on to love) this child just the same. And this child has died.

In a recent *Coronation Street* storyline (and talked about in just about every woman's magazine in the weeks that followed) a lady became pregnant. Just when things were going well, she was rushed into hospital with a miscarriage (technically the baby died in the womb rather than being miscarried, but the result is the same). However, having removed the dead child – the script went – they discovered a second baby alive. Many of the other characters then came in and didn't know if they should be happy or sad. Some said insensitive things. **The mother herself knows she must mourn the death of the baby that was her child, no matter how wonderful it is that there is (and always was) a second one**, who one day she will hold in her arms.

So is it easier or harder?

It depends on the people involved. Some people cannot handle the easiest of life's difficulties. Some thrive on the challenge to handle desperate situations together with their partner. So the ratio of problem versus personal resources available is what really counts. That is impossible to assess from outside.

THE HOSPITAL EXPERIENCE

Sometimes the visit to hospital to get 'cleaned up' after a miscarriage can make the whole process worse rather than better.

We do not work in a hospital, so it is not our business to judge people who have a different set of pressures in their world than we do in ours. But these are the words of Professor Winston (a professional in this area):

Apart from childbirth, miscarriage is about the most common reason for a younger woman to enter hospital. For this very reason hospital staff unfortunately tend to treat miscarriage as routine and do not always seem as helpful as they might be. Many doctors and nurses cannot quite understand why you may feel so frightened. Very often they are kind and reassuring but don't seem to understand that you have lost a baby who was very real to you.[2]

This seems extraordinary to us! We think something should

be done about it. When a woman goes into hospital following a miscarriage she has an awful experience called a 'scrape' (or 'D and C'). The doctors give the woman a general anaesthetic, then reach inside the womb and clear out the remains of the placenta and baby. This is not only painful but extremely personally intrusive. It should not be carried out in an officious way.

THE NEED TO KNOW WHY

This is perfectly natural. And, as a result, you will sooner or later come up with a theory. You will ask questions; analyse the days before the miscarriage took place; read books about all the possible reasons. You will then blame something or somebody; probably yourself.

But this whole process is normally futile!

Most doctors agree that it is impossible to work out why 99 per cent of miscarriages take place. If you are apportioning blame you have probably done it just for your own need for a reason; your own peace of mind. Therefore, if it is not giving you peace of mind . . . STOP IT! Most miscarriages happen because your body is made well enough to know when things are not going right. Trust that it is 'for the best', even if it does not feel that way in the heat of the moment.

THE NEED TO TALK

As with all major trauma, the process of sorting it out inside you will take time. A good two hour session with a counsellor the day after you miscarry might feel useful, but the process of grief will take longer. And will take a little patience from you and your family.

After Jacqui (Sharon's sister) had one of her miscarriages she was feeling very low. People were very kind and supportive, and that was good. But she needed some space.

A few months later there was an opportunity for us, Jacqui and my other sister (and family) to spend a couple of weeks in the Loire region of France together. What a wonderful place. We stayed in a gite – a farmhouse all by itself, surrounded by fields of wheat (that were actually harvested while we were there).

Much of the time the three of us talked. There were also all the normal family times, barbecues, board games, sunbathing, etc. But wow did we talk! We also went off (partly to let the family spend a bit of time together) and toured some of the local towns. We went on a café crawl – we recommend it. In each one we stopped, sat, drank a coffee (or Coca Cola in my case!) and yakked!

We didn't just talk about miscarriages, although that came into it. We went back over every remembered story of our whole family life. Right the way through time until Hugo got involved. We did not merely discuss the facts, but the relative good versus bads; right versus wrongs; and 'Well I was shocked!'s. We even had a few 'Really is that what happened?'s. It was great. Not just for Jacqui, but for all of us. In a happy, relaxed atmosphere, we were able to reassess the whole of our lives, values, beliefs, hopes, fears and disappointments. It gave us a chance to put everything in context. It would not have worked the day after the miscarriage. But as a therapy a bit further down the line, we recommend it.

NB: You don't have to go to France to do this . . . but it helps!

THE NEED TO MOURN

We have already spoken at some length about this in the previous chapter, but it does no harm to re-emphasise it in the very different context of miscarriage. Hear what Professor Winston has to say,

> I think it is essential to recognise that a miscarriage is a loss of life and not something that can be brushed away. You have been bereaved, and it is important to cry, to mourn. Some women find it helpful to see the placenta or remnants of their conception. Seeing the tissue, or the embryo [we prefer the word baby], helps

many come to terms with their loss. Hospital staff may
be a little wary of this, but you or your partner may ask
to see if this is possible.[3]

Other suggestions include recognising that you are in a
grief cycle, giving the child a name, holding a small funeral
service, etc.

Whatever you do, the aim of mourning is not to hold
on to the life of the baby. Rather it is to genuinely give
them over into the hands of God. To let go and let God!
Psychologists will tell you that that is the best thing you
can do; the best for your own emotional health, the best
for being able to see the future start again, and the best for
making the short life of your baby remain of value to you
and your family.

BEING ANGRY

Apart from feelings of sadness and guilt, anger is a
common emotion. However, there is little rational
basis for this – it is seldom indeed that anyone can
be said to have caused a miscarriage. Nevertheless,
it is worth knowing that your unreasonable feelings
of anger are a natural reaction to what seems to be an
unnatural event.[4]

What Professor Winston leaves out is the fact that, when
you have got over blaming yourself and everyone else, you
will almost certainly turn to *blaming God!*

My other sister, Janet, now has three children. But before
they were born she had another baby. The pregnancy went
almost full term. The doctors were going to induce her, but
decided to wait one more day. During those few extra hours
the baby died. The reason for this was toxaemia.

It was devastating. For everyone – mother, father and all
the relatives! Janet had to go through the whole process of
giving birth as if it were a healthy baby, knowing she was
dead. Tears fell. Many of them.

I find it difficult to explain exactly how I felt. I was hurt

and confused. Yes! And I was very angry. I had been a
Christian since I was very young, but this didn't fit into any
of the categories. I was angry. And I was angry with God.

I suppose prayer is one word for what I did. I went
alone and started telling God what I thought about him.
I expressed my anger in quite lurid terms. Expletive after
expletive passed my lips. I was exhausted, but I still
went on.

Then, in a strange moment of silence, I felt the presence of
someone I knew. He seemed to say, 'Have you finished?'

'No!' I bellowed. And tore into him with another list of
why the world was unreasonable and him in particular.

Every now and then I paused. He hadn't gone away.
He was still there looking at me, gently. Yes, he was
even smiling. Don't get me wrong, he wasn't laughing.
He was gently smiling and *crying!* I knew he was crying
with me . . .

'Have you finished now?'

'Yes, Father. . . . Sorry.'

How could I shout at him anymore. He didn't want the
death, the pain, the misery any more than I did. And I knew
he was there – no amount of anger could change that. And
I knew that he loved me!

If you are feeling the same, go to him and tell him. Don't
be afraid; he can handle it. After all, one of the reasons Jesus
died on the cross was to take the blame.

THE FATHER

Most people know that, after a miscarriage, most of the help
and sympathy is given to the woman. The medical staff
have to do specific things. The rest of the family say to her
how sorry they are. This makes sense in our minds because
it is inside her body that the drama has taken place.

But what about the man? How does he feel? Quite often
he is left alone serving the drinks. Quite often no one thinks
to ask him how he feels about it all.

We would like to think we have some wisdom in this
area. However having read Robert Winston's comment on

this subject we would prefer to quote him in full and leave
it at that.

> Men, too, have a very difficult time when their part-
> ner miscarries. The majority worry most about the
> woman's safety: 'What if she bleeds to death?' is a
> common but unspoken question. Men also feel sad
> or disappointed. Very often their grief will not be as
> acute, and they may find it difficult to understand
> why their partner feels so deeply. Many men also feel
> angry: 'Why us?' is commonly asked. Others resent
> the need for them to be the strong or supportive
> partner: 'I'm feeling the pain as well.' Disbelief is
> a very common feeling, as is a general sensation of
> pessimism – 'Will we ever have a baby?' – especially
> if there was difficulty in conceiving in the first place.
> Feelings of guilt at NOT feeling very distressed, or
> even being relieved at the loss of the pregnancy. At
> other times, the guilt may be because he feels that he
> caused the miscarriage by making love or by not taking
> sufficient care of his partner in other ways. Men also
> need to grieve and cry, but many feel quite inhibited
> about this and, curiously, the female partner may have
> to be quite supportive in this situation.[5]

THE FUTURE

There is good news when you have had a miscarriage. But
a silver lining is found in a cloud, so take your time before
you hear it!

The good news is that, if you can get pregnant once, you
can do it again. Letting yourself settle for a few months, and
then trying again is the best advice in most situations.

You may not like this idea initially. Having lost a baby
there can be an extreme fear of losing another. This is quite
a common feeling. Take a grip of it, and the fear will pass.
Then, assuming that's what you want, have another go!

ELEVEN

ADOPTION?

There are many options open to an infertile couple. As soon as you know you cannot have your own biological children, it leaves an enormous space in time, nurturing desire, creativity and sometimes financial resources. The most common way to mobilise all this potential gift and energy is by a couple getting involved with fostering and/or adoption.

It seems obvious. You long to be a parent. You cannot produce your own children. So care for someone else's – particularly if they are finding it hard to look after them themselves. Surely that will fill the gap? If only it were that easy!

Neither fostering nor adoption is 'like having your own'. It is a far greater challenge. In these days of open adoption, agency assessment, redefining the family unit and 'care in the community', it has to be said that the social work scene has become very complex. Most of this is very good! But it can be rather daunting for the prospective adoptive parent who does not know the rules. After all you are not a professional. You do not know the procedures or the 'right' answers to the questions.

So, as far as it is possible in writing this brief chapter, we want to give you an outline of how the adoption system works. We are not experts or professionals; but we have spoken to those who work in this field. Below are some of the perspectives they gave us, and then, at the end of the chapter, there are a number of addresses you can contact to get a fuller picture.

Let's approach this chronologically. When can you start to consider adoption?

WHEN TO START THE ADOPTION PROCESS?

The timing has to take two things into account:

1. Most agencies will not consider letting you start the process of assessment until they have cast-iron assurance that you have given up on fertility treatment of every kind. Some people do get round this – normally by lying – but it is important to realise that adopting a child is an *alternative* to giving birth to a child. (NB: Obviously you can adopt or foster other children after you have adopted or given birth to one previously. The principle above applies specifically to childless couples.) All your eggs have to be in this one basket!

   If you have not come to this conclusion yet, we suggest that you do not start by contacting an agency. It would be better to talk to someone else first: either a pastor from your local church or someone else you trust. If you find this person difficult to locate, your GP or local 'Relate' branch may be able to help.

2. On the other hand, you must not wait too long, hoping that your infertility treatment will be successful. Most agencies have an age limit where they stop allowing prospective parents to join their schemes. For some it is as young as 35. Others use a more liberal system of allowing couples to adopt a child that is 'biologically possible'. What they really mean is 'biologically normal' in the sense of couples from 35 to 40 years old will normally be allowed to adopt children who are five years old or so; because this way they will end up with a child about the same age as their contemporaries might have.

   Adopting older children can be very rewarding. However, many infertile couples only want to adopt babies (0–2 years). If this is so in your case then you must not delay too long before contacting the agencies.

   If you are worried about the policy of the agencies near you, then give them a ring and ASK!

WHICH AGENCY SHOULD WE APPLY TO?

There are three routes that are possible.

1. Most people start by contacting their **local council agency**. They are normally very good and are used to being the first port of call.

2. There are **two very good national associations** (there may be more) for adoption agencies: the BAAF (British Agencies for Adoption and Fostering) and PPIAS (Parent to Parent Information on Adoption Services). Both these addresses are at the end of the chapter. PPIAS, in particular, has local support groups where you can find other people who are struggling with the same kind of feelings and difficulties.

   Both of these will give you advice and addresses of the agencies which they recommend you contact; both the local council run agencies and the voluntary ones. (BAAF has a booklet called 'Adopting a Child' which gives a list of adoption agencies as well as information about adoption procedures and practice.) Please remember that you may well have to approach a number of agencies before you find one whose waiting list is open.

3. Finally, there is **the Christian route**. It is sometimes true that people with a real Christian faith are given quite a hard time by the adoption agencies. It can therefore be helpful to go through an agency that is specifically Christian. (Although this can sometimes backfire if the agency staff are particularly anti a certain theological standpoint within the Christian faith!) You will find a listing in the *UK Christian Handbook* or by telephoning the Evangelical Alliance (address at the end of the chapter).

   Within this category could also come an alternative to direct adoption; that is taking in a young unmarried pregnant woman. CARE Trust (address at end of chapter), and other Christian organisations who campaign against abortion, have schemes to encourage young pregnant women to keep their babies and go and live with a Christian couple through the pregnancy. Not all these women and babies stay with the couples long term, but many do.

One further thing to note is that all the agencies are looking for new parents for children with special needs. If you are prepared for this responsibility you will find that the agencies will be able to help you much more easily.

WHAT HAPPENS ONCE YOU HAVE CONTACTED THE AGENCY?

Firstly, it is important for you to realise that the adoption agencies have been set up to care for the needs **of the children.** If they are kind and nice to you, treat that as a bonus (most will be!). If you seem to have people continuously telling you their waiting list is full and not appearing to help you, do not get frustrated. They are not there to help you. You are simply offering your services to help them find homes for the children for whom they are responsible. If they do not need your services then you must look elsewhere.

The next thing we suggest is that you prepare, **beforehand,** a cv. This way you will be ready to send or say the right thing when you need to. Take time to write out who you both are and what you have done. Send this to the agency. If you make it easy for them to process you, you will have a greater chance of success.

Having said the above, each agency will have its own procedure. Each will have interviews, application forms, home assessments (normally a series of them), references and courses (normally one night a week for a month or two). It really is quite extensive and emotionally draining . . . just as if you were giving birth to a child. It has to be that way. After all they have to be sure that you are the right person and they want to be able to match you with the right child/children

WHEN DO THEY ACTUALLY START TALKING ABOUT A SPECIFIC CHILD/ CHILDREN?

Again, it depends.

You have to realise that the birth parents have rights, and that adoption is not just a kind and convenient way of looking after children; it is a **legal procedure.** Furthermore, your acceptance by the agency is not an acceptance to adopt. It is firstly an acceptance for assessment. Should this go smoothly, then you are placed on the waiting list until a child for whom you are suitable becomes their responsibility.

The legal procedure then grinds into action. There are visits by the child/children to your home. If this seems to go well, you may have them placed with you as foster parents. Assessment continues right up to and beyond the date of the court hearing. Birth mothers sometimes go all along this road giving their permission, then suddenly at the 11th hour, pull out. This is their right!

Mostly you never meet the birth parents (only exchange cards once a year or something similar). But these days even that is changing. Open adoption, particularly when adopting older children, is becoming quite common. This can even include you taking the child for regular visits back to the birth mother.

As you can tell this can all be quite traumatic. That is why the preparation needs to be extensive and careful; both for you and the child.

AT LEAST IT'S ALL OVER AFTER THE COURT HEARING?

No!

Even though legally you will be as responsible as any parent and to the outside world this baby will appear to be your son or daughter, the biological and spiritual reality has not changed.

Most adoptive parents who wax lyrical about how wonderful it all is, do this while their children are still infants. As they grow up things can often get very difficult. The agencies will teach you this in your classes if you listen. But few appreciate how hard it can be. Teenagers and young adults can be troublesome enough when they are your own flesh and blood, but adoptive children, who appear angelic as little babies, can turn out to be far more disturbed or psychologically damaged than you expect. The shock of realising the child who you have lavished your love upon has grown up to be not just ungrateful but openly hostile, can break your heart. **But . . . the risk is worth taking!** or is it? That is your decision.

There follow two stories. Both are true. Both relate to thousands of similar stories. Each express an extreme of what can happen, long term, when you adopt. Most adoptions will fall into a middle zone, with some 'not too bad' difficulties, and loads of joyful times.

Charles and Julie's Story

Charles and Julie both came to know Jesus early in life. They are upright, middle-class people, well educated and warm. The kind of people who have wisdom and gentleness; leaders of the church homegroup and youth work.

But, as with so many, soon after marriage they were not able to get pregnant. The usual medical process went into action. They were diagnosed as infertile because they were not having children – after all, what else is there to it?

Being efficient people they were soon on the adoption agency lists, going through the process of evaluation. One question they were asked was, 'If you adopt a girl and, aged 13, she comes in and says, "I'm pregnant", what will you do?' The answer was obviously good enough because they were accepted.

Time passed. The social workers started going through the selection of a child. The mother was Irish. She came to England to have the baby so that her family would not know. The whole thing was very messy! It was on, then off, then on again. Eventually they met the baby. A few more on and offs. Finally it was all legal. They had a little boy! We shall call him Michael.

They stayed on the list to get Michael a brother or sister. Again it was complex. The possible baby was being shuffled around between various of her biological mother's family members. The social workers suspected she was being abused. The days went by. The phone call came and they arranged to pick her up. She was brought back with just the grubby clothes she wore. She was totally terrified, and very dirty. Julie's mothering instinct went into overdrive. This child would now be safe. Both children would now be safe. Now . . . they had a real mum! Now they had real parents.

Let us call the little girl Carol.

The next few years were just as they imagined, apart from the process of settling the children, who were clearly emotionally damaged. But, by the time they went to school they behaved like any other kids in the community! Charles was doing very well in his job. He was the youngest project manager in his company, with a reputation for being honest, hard working and extremely good at the job. At home they moved house to a pleasant commuter town and felt that God was calling them to start a new church based in their home and then a local school – the school where their children went. A number of other families joined. It was a success.

The children grew, as they do, and before Charles and Julie knew it they were teenagers. They were doing well at school, apart from a few disciplinary problems. The teachers were puzzled, but once they knew – with the children's permission – that they were adopted, it made sense and everyone relaxed. 'It's just a phase!'

But it was not! Michael started staying out late, and being irrationally abusive. He got in with a crowd of rebellious friends. Soon drink, drugs and a deep sullenness set into his personality. Charles was always calm. Julie did what any mother would do when trying to bring discipline. But it is not always that simple.

Michael's life went slowly from bad to worse. He tried to become a chef. He moved to London. He quit job after job. He got further into drugs, raves, confusion. Every now and then he would come home. Charles and Julie always welcomed him and did their best to help. He then started having girl friends. Then one of them became pregnant; they were living together in Cornwall. Then they weren't anymore. It was getting very confusing.

Charles and Julie tried to communicate. Michael begrudgingly accepted the idea that they would give him help to buy a small house near them and move in with his partner. They thought he might have settled. He did not know Jesus, but they loved him and many kids go off the rails for a while.

Then they found him in the midst of a drugs overdose. Ambulances, hospitals, intensive care, bedsides, a close call!

They went back to the house and found that his partner's whole family had moved in. One of them had been down the road stealing all the car radios! They trashed the house, smashing everything including the toilet bowl, and smearing excrement about.

When Michael got out of hospital he stood in front of the church and apologised to those who had done their best for him. But very soon after that he was back involved in another affair. Still very confused, going to raves, etc etc.

The story continues!

Then there was Carol. At 15 she walked in and said, 'I'm pregnant!'.

Charles and Julie bit hard, went calm and asked to see her and the boy together. The two children come in apparently submissive and able to receive help. The pregnancy went as normal. Then the baby was born prematurely and was beautiful, but also suffered from spina bifida. The parents and the mother's parents spent hours, days, weeks sitting by the bed. The doctors said it was only a matter of time. It was a wonderful time of family togetherness, even in the sadness. Finally the baby died.

But how would things be for Carol? School went on. She married the boy concerned. Charles and Julie helped them with a house. Carol had another baby. Everything seemed to be settling down.

Then Carol announced, 'He's left me.'

At least in Carol's case they have stayed in a good relationship with her. She is caring and stays friendly and loving. But this has also been difficult.

'People ask us, "Is it worth it?".' Charles and Julie told us, 'and we would have to say, "Yes!". But there have been times when it was, "Only Just!"'

You might ask us why we put such a disturbing story in this book. Some people who have read this through for us have asked. 'Are you trying to put people off adoption?' The answer is no. But this is not such an unusual story.

It is important if you are set on adopting to know the problems you might face. This is the case for anybody wanting to become a parent, but the forces at work in some adoptive children are more likely to give you some problems through the early adult years. If you are prepared you are less likely to be caught by surprise.

If this puts you off, then you need to be put off. Parenting is demanding. It is one of the greatest challenges anyone can face. Don't go into it thinking otherwise.

Leighton's Story

Leighton is a distinguished, upright, Christian man in his sixties. He is a great fan of adoption. If you ask him why he says, 'I am adopted, and it has worked well for me.'

This is his story:

When I was about 12 years old, my mother told me that I was adopted. I think she handled it wisely. Until then I had never suspected that I was adopted. I should have, because my mother was barely five feet tall and my father was only about five foot six! Both of them were rather stout. I was already growing into a tall, lanky youth who would end up being six feet four.

I didn't expect anything until that cool autumn day in Toronto when my mother and I went for a walk in High Park near the apartment where her two aunts lived and where we were probably visiting at the time. Mother intimated that there had been an 'accident' of

some sort with my natural parents. At that time I
supposed that they had been killed in an accident.
Looking back I imagine that I was the 'accident'!
Mother stressed that she and my father chose to have
me because they wanted a child of their own.

From that moment on, being adopted always gave
to me a sense of being 'special', not in a sense of being
better than anybody else but in the sense of being really
loved, really chosen, and really wanted. There was an
emotional security in this.

Later on I read the Apostle Paul's words in Romans
8 v 15 that the believer is 'adopted into the bosom of his
[God's] family' which enables us to say to God, 'Father,
Father'. The Holy Spirit witnesses with us that we are
children of God and therefore we are heirs of all that
God has along with Christ (Rom 8:16&17). Paul also
taught in Galatians 4 vs 4&5 that God sent his Son
so that 'he could adopt us as his very own sons'. He
wrote to the Ephesians that God's 'unchanging plan
has always been to adopt us into his own family by
sending Jesus Christ to die for us. And did this because
he wanted to!' (Eph 1:5)

I believe that God in his providence led my parents
to choose and adopt me. What would have happened if
I had been brought up instead by my natural parents?
That's a total mystery, but I do know that in my
adopted family I was exposed at the earliest age to the
Bible, to prayer, and to influences which would lead me
not only to know God but to serve him. And what was
true of me, I believe, is true of all of us whether we are
adopted or not.

It used to be that I didn't mention very often that
I was adopted. In more recent years I frequently tell
people when I am preaching that I am adopted. Often
when I do this some adopted child or adoptive parents
will come up and say how much that meant. Some are
upset about being adopted. I remember a girl in her
early teens in Pennsylvania who said she felt 'terrible'.
I hope I was able to help her feel 'special', as I do.

A man from Greece who had immigrated to Melbourne, Australia, attended one of our meetings there and heard me mention my adoption. It rang home to him because he had been, too. The message I brought about Jesus Christ began to make more sense to him, he said, and he accepted Christ that night.

Until I was in my forties and my adopted parents had both died, I didn't think a lot about my natural parents. But in more recent years I launched a search to find out all I could about them. My quest did not go unrewarded. I wanted to know who my natural parents are to find out if I have any half-brothers or sisters living, to know something about my heritage, and especially to share with them what Jesus Christ has come to mean as the centre of my life.

All of us have the need to belong. Ultimately, that need is for more than natural or adopted parents. It is a need to be able to say to God, 'My Father'. I have read someplace that Anna Marx, the daughter of Karl Marx, the father of communism, told a friend that she had come across an old prayer which began, 'Our Father, who art in heaven'. With her secular upbringing she did not recognise the Lord's Prayer but she told her friend wistfully, 'If there really was a God like the one described in that prayer, I could believe in him.'

As an adopted son of the heavenly Father I would like to say, 'Anna, he is real. He is a home for all your longings. Believe in him.'[1]

For Leighton adoption worked out well. From ordinary beginnings he became one of the most respected Christian leaders in the world. He was, as you might work out from the way he tells his own story, an associate evangelist with the Billy Graham Evangelistic Association. He then went on to chair the boards of some of the most strategic initiatives in the history of God's people. He now runs his own organisation 'Leighton Ford Ministries' and invests his energy in the next generation of Christian leaders. So maybe we could say that his adoption has worked out well for all of us – even for the world!

Hopefully this story has given the needed balance to the previous one!

Postscript

As anyone who knows the details can tell, this has been a very sketchy approach to adoption. If you want more detail we suggest you contact these organisations:

BAAF (British Agencies for Adoption and Fostering)
11 Southwark Street, London. SE1 1RQ
tel: 0171–407 8800
fax: 0171–403 6970

Millgrove Christian Childcare Network
tel: 0181–504 2702

PCCA (Promoting Christian Childcare Alternatives)
tel: 0122 667207 David and Pauline Pearson

PPIAS (Parent to Parent information on Adoption Services)
Lower Boddington, Daventry, Northamptonshire. NN11 6YB
tel: 0327 60295

If you are interested in a list of Christian adoption agencies, you can find them in the **UK Christian Handbook** or by contacting:

EA (The Evangelical Alliance)
Whitefield House, 186 Kennington Park Road, London. SE11 4BT
tel: 0171–582 0228
fax: 0171–582 6221

If you are interested in caring for single pregnant women, please write for more details to:

CARE
53 Romney St, London, SW1P 3RF

TWELVE

EVERY CLOUD HAS . . . ?

'Sing, O barren woman,
you who never bore a child;
burst into song, shout for joy,
you who were never in labour;
because more are the children of the desolate woman
than of her who has a husband.'
(Isaiah 54:1)

[Those] who do their best always do more, though they be
haunted by a sense of failure. . . . Be good and true; be patient;
be undaunted. Leave your usefulness to God to estimate. He
will see to it that you do not live in vain.
(George Morrison, Scottish minister)[1]

'Yes, but what are we going to do?' we hear you say. 'We thought a great chunk of our time, energy and money were going to be invested in children. If we are not going to have any, what shall we do?'

The first thing to say is that you must do *something*! This is not just to deaden the pain of being childless; nothing will do that effectively. Nor is it just to mobilise your instincts for parenting, although there is a great amount of power locked up in that part of you that needs using. Nor is it just to make your life mean something; your life means something anyway.

No, it is bigger than all these. It is because God made you for something more than being upset about what you cannot have. 'For we are God's workmanship, created in Christ Jesus to do good works, which God prepared in advance for us to do' (Eph 2:10).

If the good works that God has prepared for you to do
are not bringing up your own biological children, then it
is your responsibility to find out what they are. Many
childless couples are doing some wonderful things which
they may not have been able or motivated to do if they
had been investing in offspring. You must become one
of them.

Posterity. That is the key word.

Posterity means 'the future generations of people who
live on this planet' – at least until the Lord Jesus returns,
then posterity will be all that exists in the new heaven and
new earth. We must leave *something* for posterity. If we can
do that, leave something that we are justifiably proud of,
we can honestly say, 'Our lives were not in vain!' We can
one day look into the face of Jesus in heaven and say, 'I
have invested all that you gave me!' And we may expect
to hear the reply, 'Well done, good and faithful servant!'

The aim of this chapter is to help you at least to start
looking for the kind of thing you could invest your lives
and parental instincts in. We are going to list some 'good
ideas'. Some you will think are 'not you'. Others you may
think are stupid. But maybe one or two will at least help
you in the direction of finding a silver lining in the cloud
of your childlessness.

1. Adoption

This is still the most usual way forward. The most
important thing is not to put it off too long. If you think
you may be infertile and have started investigations,
start talking with each other about adoption. If this is
something you both would consider, then start getting
in touch with agencies.

2. Fostering

This can happen in many ways. There is the official
route, via social workers etc. It is hard work, emotionally demanding, and you have to give the children back
at the end. But you may have the privilege of investing
in numerous children through your life time.

Alternatively there are unofficial versions. In their book *God Gave me a Dream*,[2] Norman and Grace Barnes explain how they found themselves, to be infertile. They then tell of how a family went to live abroad and the teenage daughter came to live in their home. She grew up, got married, and now lives across the street. When she had her first baby – Stephanie – Norman and Grace started being called Grandma and Grandad. (There are other wonderful stories in that chapter of their book – read it if you can!)

3. **Being involved with a relative or friend's child**
When our nephew, Matthew, was born, his mother handed him to me saying, 'Here's the child you'll never have. Share mine!' In a real way we have been able to be involved with Matthew and his two sisters, and have worked out some of our parental needs. This has happened to a lesser degree with some other friends, although we have become very wary of people asking us to be godparents – it sometimes comes from an over-active sympathy.

Grace and Norman Barnes are better at this than us. Good friends of theirs – who knew of their infertility – involved them completely in the birth and nurture of their first child; even putting a cot in their house so she could stay with them. What we suggest is that whatever works for you is probably a good thing.

4. **Extended family or community living**
There is a housing shortage. There are millions of lonely people. There are childless people who would love to be involved with nurturing. There are parents who are overstretched financially and with time commitments. Cannot we, as God's people, begin to model real examples of caring extended households, where these kinds of needs are met. It is not for everyone. But if it is for you, why not take the initiative and organise it.

5. **Spiritual children**
    In Isaiah 54 the prophet is shouting that there will come
    a time when being a Christian will be more important
    than being alive, and that those who can bring people
    to new birth and nurture them in that spiritual life with
    God will have more influence and credit in heaven than
    those with merely physical babies. If you are not yet a
    Christian you will not yet appreciate this. It is none the
    less true.

    Jesus remained single and childless, but he invested
    in 12 men plus a group of women. Not all of them
    lived up to his hopes (Judas even betrayed him).
    But children are like that. Through that small group
    Jesus started a community that will exist forever.
    As you follow him he wants you to do something
    similar.

    Elizabeth Mittelstaedt is infertile. Her magazine,
    Lydia, influences over 60,000 women across Europe
    every month.

    > 'I remember one meeting where I was speaking and
    > several women stood up to accept the Lord as their
    > Saviour. I felt God say, 'These are your children,
    > born into the Kingdom – it's just a different way
    > to give life.'
    > Today when I receive letters from readers who
    > say, 'I didn't abort my baby, and I'm naming her
    > Lydia after the magazine,' my heart is thrilled. It's
    > been so healing to me.[3]

6. **Career**
    One of the things infertile couples find easier than
    those with children is having a career together. It
    may be your own business; it may not. It may be
    specifically children-orientated; it may not. We recently
    heard about a childless couple who for years have been
    responsible for the production of children's books at
    Lion Publishing. They have invested their lives; and
    their lives are bearing fruit.

7. **Church**
   Obviously this is *our* main idea! We have invested our
   lives into Christian ministry and bringing a church to
   birth. But some will say, that's all right for you; God
   has called and gifted you in that way. What about us
   with our other careers still going on?

   Robert and Catherine Sweatman are a good example
   of that. Robert is a high-flying consultant. Catherine is
   a very busy GP. They are also childless.

   They belong to a Baptist church in the south of
   England. After joining they took a long hard look at
   where they could be most useful. They had limited time
   and wanted it all to count. Robert was asked to be a dea-
   con, but refused as he still was not clear on what they
   should do. Then they offered to take responsibility for
   the entire package of childrens' ministries in the church.
   Their plan was to run a large summer holiday club and
   ongoing clubs for all ages through the year. Once it
   was agreed, they brought all their efforts and talents
   to bear. Not only has the church got a fabulous and
   effective children's programme, Robert and Catherine
   are enjoying mobilising their parental instincts.

8. **Creative work**
   Whoever heard of a mother with small children having
   time to run a drama company, mould a sculpture,
   become an expert in fine art, write short stories for
   radio, lead historical trips to Israel, put a band together,
   plant a beautiful garden? Yes, it surely has been done
   even by those with small children. But if this is the kind
   of thing you have always wanted to make happen, this
   is an opportunity you must not let slip through your
   fingers.

9. **Finance**
   Children cost money. Those that do not have children quite often have greater quantities of spare cash.
   There are endless possibilities of what this can make
   happen.

David and Claire Sladden are two more friends of ours who do not have children. As Christians they have always started their financial giving with a 10 per cent tithe. However, as they realised that they had spare money they decided to double tithe. Now their bottom line for financial giving is 20 per cent. Through this, David and Claire have been able to put money into projects which are advancing their dreams and purposes in this world. It has also helped to open doors that would otherwise have stayed closed both to them and the gospel.

10. Social action for the disadvantaged

Very soon after our wedding, our best man's wife walked out on him. It was a tragedy and almost destroyed him. For a couple of years he was in a bit of a daze. He had quite a high-powered job but knew he needed to get out of suits and make his life count for something. He eventually joined the Shaftesbury Society as the senior worker at one of their hostels for homeless teenagers in London. Although childlessness was not what broke up his marriage, caring for these lost young men has revolutionised his life. There are days when he hates it. What parent doesn't? But he knows he is doing something that really matters. There is a light in his eye.

If you are childless, we recommend you look into focussing your career, home and energy on something that really matters. You have a privilege. You are free from any excuses. You can make a difference while others feel obliged to maintain the middle-class nightmare, for the sake of the children.

As Michael Card wrote in his song 'Distressing Disguise':

He is in the pain, He is in the need.
He is in the poor; we are told to feed.
Though he was rich, for us He became poor:
How could he give so much? What was it for?

In His distressing disguise
He waits for us to surmise
That we rob our brothers by all that we own,
And that's not the way He has shown.

Every time a faithful servant serves a brother that's
   in need
What happens at that moment is a miracle indeed.
As they look at one another in an instant it is clear:
Only Jesus is visible for they've both disappeared.

He is in the hand that reaches out to give.
He is in the touch that causes men to live.
So speak with your life now as well as your tongue.
Shelter the homeless and care for the young.

In His distressing disguise
He hopes that we'll realise
That when we take care of the poorest of them
We've really done it to him.[4]

So, there are some ideas to get you thinking.

Don't spend the rest of your life holding out a forlorn hope of healing. Some hold candles for lost loves all their lives, and it does not do them or anyone else the slightest bit of good.

Stop asking, 'Why can't I . . . ?'

Start asking, 'What can I do?'

Jesus said, 'Provide purses for yourselves that will not wear out, a treasure in heaven that will not be exhausted, where no thief comes near and no moth destroys. For where your treasure is, there your heart will be also' (Luke 12:33,34).

Many do have children. Some of them succeed both in nurturing those children and investing their life in this world. But so many only leave disappointment, distrust and damage in the next generation. Losing a teenager to a rebellious lifestyle can sometimes be worse than never having a child at all. If you did have a child it would only be one of God's children that you were looking after. So why not invest your life for the sake of the rest of God's children, while you have the chance.

THIRTEEN

BUT . . . BUT . . . BUT . . .

So you know what we think. But what do you think? At this point in a book you will normally have either loved it or shelved it. Some may be in between. Hopefully you understand and accept the general direction we have taken. But, possibly, you have some 'But . . . s', If so this chapter should help.

We have tried to think of as many 'But . . . s' as we can; then to write a response to each. See if any of them scratch where you are itching.

BUT THIS JUST MAKES ME ANGRY

The most interesting thing about infertility is that you may have read everything we have written, agreed with 90 per cent and *still* be angry. Even as you analyse yourself you cannot quite work out why. Somewhere deep inside something of what we are saying has not yet met where you are at. You picked up this book with hope in your heart, and now you are disappointed!

Don't worry! It's OK to feel like that. It is very rare that black and white on paper can ever be certain to completely reach a person who reads it. But instead of getting angry with us, take a good look at that part of you that you feel we have not touched. I expect you will learn more about your response to infertility by doing that than anything else.

The problem is that you are probably looking for a rational reason for why you are still so angry.

'Whoever said your feelings had to be rational?' That's what one of the childless men said to us half way through trying to share with us how he felt about not being able to

make his wife conceive. He is an intelligent, well-educated
and articulate man. But when it came to his grief and anger
and feelings towards others who have tried to advise him,
he admitted to being far from rational. What is more, he
gloried in the fact. He said it made him know he was flesh,
blood and the image of God; not just a computer.

So if you are feeling things that don't make sense, don't
just push them away. Take time and learn about yourself.
It may be the most important thing you ever do.

BUT I THOUGHT READING THIS BOOK WOULD TAKE MY PAIN AWAY

One of the phrases that has helped us more than any other
over the last year came from a seminar on counselling by
a psychologist and pastor called John Adlington. He said,
'Who gave you the right to try to take people's pain away?
Even God doesn't do that!'

He's right you know. Pain – physical or emotional –
doesn't feel nice. But it has its purpose. As C.S. Lewis said,
'Pain is God shouting at the world that something is wrong.'

If we did not feel pain when we placed our hand in the
fire, we might leave it there. Then we would cause more
and more damage. Pain has a purpose. It motivates us to
get things sorted out. It empowers us to change things so
that the healing process can start. It reveals; and guides the
eye and hand to the source of the discomfort. It even hints
at the kind of treatment that might be most appropriate.

Just because a first-aid course can tell you how to deal
with pain does not mean to say just reading it will remove
that pain. But if you take the advice; treat the trouble; you
will soon find things begin to improve, assuming that is
medically – or miraculously – possible.

BUT YOU HAVE NOT GONE INTO MUCH DETAIL ON THE ETHICS SIDE

There are many levels on which you can write a book.
You can write for the academics, who revel in the words

and love teasing out the essence of the argument. Then there are the professionals; in this case the medics. They are struggling with making the right decisions on a day by day basis. They already read journal after journal on the subject. Even the Christian medical staff have a whole load of pamphlets carefully dissecting each technique and the applicable verses from the Bible.

Or you can write for the people on the coal face; the ones feeling the pain and having to make personal choices. If you become too complex you lose them. If too shallow, you lose the desired effect. You have to deal with the things that matter to them and that relate to the decisions they will have to make.

This book is for this latter group.

We are not academics; in the ivory tower sense of that phrase.

We are not medics; even though we do understand the difference between Gametes and Zygotes and also understand that the actual moment an egg becomes a baby is medically difficult to pin down. We also understand why there are arguments about where and when not to experiment on human embryos. Even though we do know all of these things, we do not think that this is the place to rehearse them all. We also believe passionately that life starts at the moment of conception. If you are disappointed with us on that score, we apologise; ask your forgiveness; and suggest you write us a letter. As far as we are able, we shall respond. If it is beyond our expertise, we will refer you to the appropriate quarter.

BUT OUR MARRIAGE IS REALLY UNDER PRESSURE

We feel for you. In every life there are times when a storm comes. In some marriages storms come even more often. Infertility can be one of the worst storms you will ever face. If it is getting rough then don't just sit there . . . *get some help!*

Sorry to shout. But if you need help, ask for it. You could try and contact Relate (although their waiting lists are getting very long at present) or, even better, drop us a

line at Grassroots (c/o The Grassroots Office, 99 Mayshame,
Barnet, Herts EN5 2DX). Apart from being able to write back,
we are also in touch with Christian churches all over the
country. In many of them there are trained counsellors.
They will either talk to one or both of you together.

No matter how bad it is, if you *now* stop feeding what
is pulling you apart, and *now* start feeding all that draws
you together, then *now* all is not lost.

We hesitate to give any more advice than that. After all
every couple is different. There may be all sorts of reasons
why you are finding being infertile very difficult. You need
someone to take you seriously; to sit down and listen to
you. You need someone who is not looking for an 'off the
peg' solution. Someone who, with the help of God the Holy
Spirit, will listen and 'tailor make' their response to you.

> But now, this is what the LORD says—
> 'Fear not, for I have redeemed you;
> I have summoned you by name; you are mine.
> When you pass through the waters,
> I will be with you;
> and when you pass through the rivers,
>   they will not sweep over you.
> When you walk through the fire,
>   you will not be burned;
>   the flames will not set you ablaze.
> For I am the LORD, your God,
>   the Holy One of Israel, your Saviour.
> (Isaiah 43:1–3)

BUT MY MOTHER/FATHER WANTS TO BE A GRANDPARENT

To be honest, so do ours! But that is never a good reason
to have a child.

One Christmas we got a 'scare'. We thought that my
period had not come. We got ourselves all worked up.
We started trying to work out all the implications. It was
quite fun really. And the best part was the thought that

we could go over Christmas Day and say, 'We've got a
real present for you!' You see my (Hugo's) Mum has had
four children. And up to quite recently, none of them had
produced a grandchild. We know she was upset about it.
But what can you do?

Suffice it to say, we had obviously got the counting of
days all muddled up. There was evening and there was
morning, and then my period arrived. It was a sad moment.
And yet also a relief. Strange that, isn't it?

FOURTEEN

ONE DAY!

'This is not my home. I'm just passing through.'

Having begun at the beginning it is only fitting that we should end with the end. The end of the Bible that is. In Revelation we read a description of those who will be in heaven:

> After this I looked and there before me was a great multitude that no-one could count, from every nation, tribe, people and language, standing before the throne and in front of the Lamb. They were wearing white robes and holding palm branches in their hands.
>
> (Rev 7:9)

One of the cults of the modern world is the worship of family. We don't mean family in the general sense, but family in the sense of 'my family' for each of us. On *Eastenders* (BBC TV) Pauline is always saying, 'It doesn't matter about anything else as long as we keep the family together.' We think this thinking is rooted spiritually in the same place as *racism*. It also relates closely to the worship of ancestors that is practised all over the East.

The truth is that the populating of the world can as easily be done by our next door neighbour as ourselves. As it is many so-called experts are saying the world's next crisis will be over-population.

But hold on a moment. Isn't it the populating of heaven that matters the most? Of course it would be a good feeling to know that a child of yours had made it there, but

your children will never be the only people who need
to know the way; nor is the populating of heaven simply
dependent on a particular type of person having babies!
Assuming you do go to heaven, you will find that the
only family there is Jesus' family; and it will be more
multi-coloured than you can imagine!

Blood is thicker than water. That's what people say, isn't it?

But Jesus' blood is thicker than any family bloodline. And
in eternity it will be the only blood that counts.

The key to entrance into the Kingdom of God is not
having a child; it is becoming like a child. Childlike faith
is faith like Abraham's. Let's see what God said to him:

> Leave your country, your people and your father's
> household and go to the land I will show you.
> 'I will make you into a great nation
>   and I will bless you;
> I will make your name great,
>   and you will be a blessing.
> I will bless those who bless you,
>   and whoever curses you I will curse;
> and all peoples on earth
>   will be blessed through you.'
>
> (Gen 12:1–3)

Can you see the principle. It is only as you leave behind
your natural obsession with country, race and family that
you can truly enter into the blessing of God. But if you
enter that blessing, you may bring blessing and life – even
spiritual children – to every people on earth.

Elizabeth Mittelstaedt was asked, 'What would you say
to encourage those who are facing infertility?'

She said,

> First, I think you should try every medical avenue.
> After that, turn it over to God and trust that he has
> a special plan for you. I've found that many women
> who've wanted to give life and couldn't are 'giving
> life' in other areas.

   Second, don't live in a state of waiting. Through
those years I kept saying, 'I'll get pregnant *next* month.'
And I waited and waited and waited. One day I
realised my life was passing by, and I wasn't living.[1]

In the words of Scripture:

   . . . Since we are surrounded by such a great cloud
   of witnesses, *let us throw off everything that hinders* . . .
   and let us run with perseverance the race marked out
   for us. Let us fix our eyes on Jesus, the author and
   perfector of our faith, who for the joy set before him
   endured the cross, scorning its shame, and sat down
   at the right hand of the throne of God. Consider him
   who endured such opposition from sinful men, so that
   you will not grow weary and lose heart.

                          (Heb 12:1–3; italics ours)

There is so much to do. There is so little time in which to
do it. In a fallen world there is no one who has all the
things they think they need to make them completely
happy. What's more, there is no one who is as happy as
God intends them to be. Each of us feels the struggle of
'the whole creation' as it 'has been groaning as in the pains
of childbirth right up to the present time' (Rom 8:22).
   If you feel things are not perfect in your world, join the
club! Then let us, together, join our hands with the Lord
Jesus. Let us grab this world by the guts and start making
it a better place to live in. And let us grab the people of
this world, introduce them to Jesus, recruit them for the
same purpose, and start getting them ready for the next.
And through every trial or low feeling let us look to Jesus,
who has been there before us, overcome, and called us to
follow him in being overcomers.
   Look to Jesus, and remember. Remember it is he who has
promised us a new heaven. It is he who has promised us a
new earth, with no more tears or crying. And it is he who
has promised us a light, both at the end of the darkness,
and in it.

FURTHER READING

Getting Pregnant by Professor Robert Winston MB BS FRCOG (Pan). This is the complete guide to fertility and infertility by the UK medical profession's leading spokesperson on the subject. Easy to understand and a useful guide to terms and medical approaches.

Two's Company by Mike and Katey Morris (Kingsway). Through the pages of Katey's diary we see an honest and moving account of a Christian couple facing up to the hopes, disappointments, medical tests, marriage pressures, well-meaning advice and pain connected with them finding themselves to be infertile.

God Gave me a Dream by Norman Barnes (New Wine Press). In this autobiographical book that describes a life of Christian ministry, one chapter is devoted to Norman and Grace's realisation that they were infertile and the struggles and victories that came out of the feelings and circumstances that followed.

Why us Lord? by Joy Cooke (Pickering Paperbacks). Explores the feelings of those who are childless. Chris and Mary Key say that it was especially helpful because it seemed to put their feelings into words, and this showed that they were not alone.

Childless: The Hurt and the Hope by Beth Spring (Lion). A pocketbook that seeks to dispel a lot of myths surrounding childlessness, and offers a number of alternatives and plenty of hope.

The Ache for a Child by Debra Bridwell (Victor Books). Bridwell presents information on infertility and pregnancy from the American perspective, and interweaves this with her own experiences.

Preconceived Ideas edited by The Church of Scotland Board of Social Responsibility (St Andrew's Press). This provides a Christian perspective of fertilisation and embryology.

Trying for a Baby by Peter Moore (Lion). Explores medical and moral dilemmas involved in different fertilisation treatments without providing specific answers.

NOTES

Chapter 1

1. 'Innocence Lost', from *Angels of Mercy* album by Susan Ashton. Words by Karey and Wayne Kirkpatrick © 1992 Emily Boothe Inc/Magic Beans Music/Holy Molar Music (admin by Reunion Music Group Inc).

Chapter 2

1. 'All of my Hope', author's name withheld.

Chapter 3

1. Elizabeth Mittelstaedt (editor of *Lydia* Christian Magazine) *Today's Christian Woman*, Jan/Feb 1992.
2. If you wish to understand this more fully, we suggest you get hold of an excellent book by Derek Prince called *Blessing or Curse, You Can Choose* (Milton Keynes, Word Publishing).

Chapter 5

1. 'Taking the best route to treating infertility', Susannah Benady, MIMS Magazine Weekly 26 October 1993.
2. Ibid.

Chapter 6

1. Story told by Ellie Mumford and recorded at St Paul's Church, Onslow Square, London 5 June 1994.
2. Chris and Mary Key live in South London, where Chris is in charge of Emmanuel, West Dulwich.

Chapter 10

1. Professor Robert Winston, *Getting Pregnant* (London, Pan).
2. Ibid.
3. Ibid.
4. Ibid.
5. Ibid.

Chapter 11

1. Leighton Ford in *A Life Surprised*.

Chapter 12

1. George H. Morrison, *The Wind on the Heath* (London, Hodder & Stoughton, 1915) p10.
2. Norman and Grace Barnes, *God Gave me a Dream* (Bognor Regis, New Wine Press, 1988).
3. Elizabeth Mittelstaedt in *Today's Christian Woman*. Jan/Feb 1992.
4. 'Distressing Disguise' from the album *Present Reality* by Michael Card. © 1988 Word Music UK.

Chapter 14

1. Elizabeth Mittelstaedt in *Today's Christian Woman*.